Eyes tightly closed, she swayed against him.

Even now her traitorous body was still alive to those skilled, seductive hands, making it hard for her to remain clear-headed. She laced her fingers around the back of his head and stretched up, covering his face with small, feverish, open-mouthed kisses.

'Oh, James,' Katherine murmured huskily, 'James...'

Daniel's reaction was as immediate as she'd hoped. His body stiffened against her and he drew away, his arms dropping to his side.

'It was a slip...I'm sorry,' she whispered.

Dear Reader

We are always keen at Mills & Boon to discover more about our readers' likes and dislikes. This month, we want to know what you think about our heroes! He is always in command and always a real catch, but do you like your hero to be just that little bit on the side of dangerous—ruthless even? Or do you like him to be gentle and caring, and unashamed to show it?

Do you like a gentleman or a rake? And what about foreign heroes? We'd love to know so put pen to paper and tell us.

The Editor

Rosemary Gibson was born in Egypt. She spent the early part of her childhood in Greece and Vietnam, and now lives in the New Forest. She has had numerous jobs, ranging from working with handicapped children, collecting litter, and being a petrol pump attendant, to airline ground hostess, but she has always wanted to be a writer. She was lucky enough to have her first short story accepted eight years ago and now writes full time. She enjoys swimming, playing hockey, gardening and travelling.

HIDDEN IN THE PAST

BY

ROSEMARY GIBSON

MILLS & BOON LIMITED
ETON HOUSE   18-24 PARADISE ROAD
RICHMOND   SURREY   TW9 1SR

*First published in Great Britain 1992
by Mills & Boon Limited*

© Rosemary Gibson 1992

*Australian copyright 1992
Philippine copyright 1992
This edition 1992*

ISBN 0 263 77757 X

*Set in Times Roman 10 on 12 pt.
01-9210-55680 C*

Made and printed in Great Britain

CHAPTER ONE

THE lanky, fair-haired boy paused in front of the stall at the far end of the cobbled market square and gazed disparagingly at the produce on sale. 'Organic vegetables,' he sniffed witheringly. 'It's just a big con to charge exorbitant prices.'

The smaller figure by his side gazed up at him with horror. 'You'd prefer to stuff your body full of chemicals, risk destroying the landscape and wildlife, just to save a few miserable pence?' she demanded fiercely. In a clear carrying voice she began to extol the virtues of the natural method of food production that worked with nature instead of against it.

The scepticism on the boy's face faded. Enlightenment dawned in its wake. 'You're right,' he sighed, looking suitably chastened. 'What's money compared to health?' Theatrically he threw his arms wide open, symbolically embracing the world. 'And helping to preserve this green and pleasant land of ours?' Squaring his shoulders manfully, he turned his attention to the slim girl behind the market stall. 'A dozen lettuce, six pounds of broad beans and a bunch of those delicious radishes, please,' he requested enthusiastically.

With unruffled clear green eyes Katherine Maitland surveyed the grinning faces of her younger brother and his twin sister. 'No Oscars today. In fact, I should sack your script writer,' she advised, stooping to pick up an empty crate, which she deposited in the back of the van

5

drawn up alongside the stall. 'I'm selling vegetables, not ham.'

'Corn not in season at the moment, then?' Timothy enquired, and guffawed appreciatively at his schoolboy wit.

Her lips twitching, Katherine stood up and flicked back a strand of thick corn-coloured hair that had escaped the confines of the pony-tail cascading down her back. 'How did maths go?' she asked, and received an incoherent grunt from her brother, which she correctly interpreted as meaning that the exam had been well within his ability.

Jessica was more forthcoming. 'Absolutely foul,' she announced cheerfully. 'Still, never mind. Only three weeks to go and then that's it.' She threw a challenging glance at her sister. 'No more exams, no more school.'

Katherine refused to take the bait, in no mood to take up the cudgels of battle at present. But she silently reaffirmed her vow that somehow during the summer holidays she was going to persuade Jessica to remain in full-time education until she was eighteen. It was what their parents would have wanted, of that she had no doubt.

Her eyes flickered over to the twins as with practised ease they began to fold up the trestle-table, observing ruefully the expanse of wrist revealed beneath Tim's jacket. He grew out of his clothes with alarming speed and she inherited a steady stream of voluminous sweaters which were ideal for working out of doors in the winter. With his sensitive face, dreamy eyes and habitual air of vague preoccupation, Tim's physical appearance was misleading and totally belied his cheerful, intensely practical, down-to-earth nature.

Jessica, in contrast, was small and volatile, her life a dramatic succession of triumphs and disasters which she generously shared with her not always attentive or sympathetic siblings. Her blonde hair formed bubbly curls over her head and her rounded curves were already beginning to attract male attention, much to Katherine's consternation. Naïvely, perhaps, she'd assumed that her role of surrogate parent would become easier as the twins grew older; instead she seemed simply to be encountering a different and more complex set of problems.

'You must stop being so protective. The twins aren't children any more,' James had chided her only a few months ago. In the same way he'd gently suggested in the early days that spoiling Jesse and Tim wasn't the ideal way of compensating for the loss of their parents.

She'd been nineteen, just completing her first year at horticultural college, when they'd been killed in a car crash. One minute she'd been a carefree, self-indulgent student; the next she'd found herself responsible for the lives of two frightened, grief-stricken twelve-year-olds. Katherine's eyes darkened with painful recollections. She'd never have coped over the last four years, she admitted honestly, without James's unstinting moral support.

Absently she began to pack up the remaining vegetables into a crate. Not too many left, she thought with a rush of satisfaction. Taking the stall in the Tuesday market had been something of a gamble but it was one that had paid off, and she was beginning to build up a core of regular, satisfied weekly customers. While she'd been daydreaming Tim had dismantled the overhead canopy and stowed it in the van, Katherine registered with gratitude. Slamming the rear doors closed, she walked around to the front of the van and clambered up into the driver's seat beside Tim, who had fished out a textbook from his school bag and was studying it assiduously.

'Where's Jesse?' Katherine asked, and then spotted her sister on the opposite side of the square, talking animatedly to a camouflaged figure astride a motorbike.

She's sixteen, Katherine reminded herself firmly. She couldn't wrap Jessica in cotton wool forever.

'Who was that?' she murmured with contrived casualness as Jessica bounded up, flushed and happy.

'Just a boy I know. He's asked me to go to a party with him next Saturday.' Jessica heaved a sigh as she saw the expression on her sister's face. 'Nearly all the girls in my class have boyfriends,' she complained, and added pointedly, 'You were always out with James when you were my age.'

But that had been different, Katherine thought silently. She'd known James Sinclair all her life. Their respective fathers had been partners in a firm of Salisbury accountants, a firm which James, after completing his exams, had also joined.

'You're not going on the back of his motorbike,' Katherine said adamantly. 'I'll give you a lift and pick you up afterwards.'

Jessica looked skywards, shrugged and climbed up into the van beside her twin.

Katherine turned the ignition key and the engine spluttered weakly and faded. 'Damn,' she cursed under her breath. She'd noticed a warning light on the dashboard flickering on and off over the past few days but she'd ignored it, hoping with the optimism of the non-mechanically minded that the fault, if left unattended, might somehow miraculously rectify itself.

'Shall I have a look?' Tim offered, but Katherine shook her head. She knew that Tim would cheerfully spend the rest of the afternoon and evening tinkering about with the engine, but she rather regretfully decided that his time would be more profitably employed revising for his next exam tomorrow. She flicked a glance at the clock on the church tower at the far end of the square.

'If you hurry, you should catch the bus.'

'What will you do?' Tim demanded, unwilling to desert her in the present emergency.

'I'll go and see James.' James had nursed the elderly van for years, coaxing it through its annual MOT and saving her, Katherine admitted, a small fortune in garage bills. 'He's taking a few days off before the wedding, so he should be at home this afternoon.' She'd half hoped James might appear at the market stall at some stage during the day. 'Come on, dynamic duo, or you'll miss the bus,' she continued hastily. 'Oh, and if I'm not back by then, there's cold chicken and——'

'Salad for supper,' the twins chorused in unison and, muttering darkly about cholesterol deprivation and the disadvantages of possessing a sister who ran a market garden, they leapt from the van and raced across the square towards the approaching bus. Katherine grinned slightly—their staple diet during the summer months did tend to be rather monotonous!

She gave a quick, cursory glance at herself in the driving mirror, wishing that she had a lipstick with her— or even a comb, for that matter. Releasing her hair from the pony-tail, she raked a hand through the thick waves, letting them tumble down to her shoulders. She had no illusions about her looks—her candid siblings had made certain of that! 'You're not exactly pretty,' Jessica had informed her thoughtfully on one occasion, 'but you've a sort of interesting face.'

'Your eyes aren't bad,' Timothy had chipped in with masculine authority. 'And you look OK when you smile.'

Katherine grinned at the recollection, perfectly aware of her own shortcomings. Her mouth was too wide, her chin too determined, her nose with a faint dusting of tiny freckles too nondescript for conventional beauty. Her only redeemable features as far as she was concerned were the long dark lashes framing her wide-spaced, clear green eyes.

She locked the van and began to walk along the high street of the small Wiltshire town, tucking her hair into the hood of her waterproof jacket as it began to drizzle with rain, the grey clouds that had scudded threateningly across the June sky all day finally releasing their burden. At least it would save watering outside tonight, she supposed. Would it rain on Saturday? What was that saying about lucky being the bride on whom the sun shone? Was the reverse also true? Her stomach muscles contracted involuntarily. Four days to go before the wedding. There was still time for James to change his mind, to realise he might be making the biggest mistake of his life ... Katherine came to an abrupt halt, appalled by her line of thought. This has got to stop, she told herself forcefully. She was twenty-three years old, for Pete's sake, not some adolescent with an over-active imagination. Did she seriously think, even for a second, that James would jilt his bride at this late stage in the proceedings?

With renewed briskness she continued on down the street, turned left into a cul-de-sac and paused in front of the Victorian cottage that she had helped James choose when he'd announced his intention of leaving the family home and buying his own house. Undeterred by the cottage's dilapidated state, they'd both immediately seen its potential, their ideas for modification and improvements coinciding exactly. But then she and James had always agreed about everything. Even as children they had never squabbled.

She unlatched the front gate and walked up the stone-flagged path, inspecting the colourful borders, ablaze with the flowers she herself had planted last spring. Automatically she bent down and tugged at a dandelion, wrestling with the long roots until they came up in her hand, and walked slowly up to the door. She pressed the bell, envisaging the smile on James's face, the warmth in his deep brown eyes at her unexpected appearance, and was disconcerted to realise that she was feeling quite ridiculously nervous.

The door swung open and Katherine's face fell.

'What are you doing here?' she demanded bluntly, looking up into a pair of lazy hazel-gold eyes. 'I thought you weren't due to arrive until Thursday.'

Leaning back against the door-jamb, arms folded indolently across his chest, Daniel Sinclair surveyed her in silence for one long, full minute, his face devoid of any expression. 'After an absence of over two years, I'm deeply touched by your ecstatic greeting,' he drawled finally and, swinging round abruptly on his heel, retreated into the cottage, leaving the front door open behind him.

Katherine shrugged, and, hesitating only momentarily, crossed the threshold and closed the door. Daniel's manner hadn't improved with the passage of time, she thought acidly, following the tall, lean figure down the narrow tiled hall. Had it really been over two years since she'd last seen James's elder brother? He normally returned to the family home each Christmas but, come to think of it, he had failed to materialise over the past

couple of festive seasons. Not that she'd missed him,
she admitted. If anything, she'd been relieved by his absence. Even over Christmas she found it difficult to
extend goodwill towards Daniel Sinclair.

'Can I fetch a vase for your dandelion?' he enquired
gravely as they entered the square-shaped living-room
that overlooked the secluded back garden.

Katherine ignored him, removed her damp jacket and
without waiting to be asked sat down on the edge of an
armchair. After all, this was James's home, not Daniel's;
he was merely staying here until Saturday, as his parents'
house would be fully occupied by the horde of relatives
descending for the imminent wedding.

'When did you arrive back?' She addressed him
without much interest. Back from where? she suddenly
wondered, frowning slightly. Australia? America? Where
exactly was Daniel working at the moment? She dragged
through the recesses of her mind but failed to produce
an answer. The trouble was, she simply switched off
whenever any member of the Sinclair family mentioned
Daniel's name, irritated by the swell of pride that crept
into their voices. After qualifying as an architect, Daniel
had gained international acclaim early on in his career
and now travelled all over the world, in the enviable position of being able to pick and choose those commis-
sions which most appealed to him. The recipients of
countless awards, his imaginative yet practical designs
featured regularly in the glossy Sunday magazines. But
Katherine remained determinedly unimpressed by his
achievements, had always refused point-blank to attend
any award ceremony with James and his parents, the
thought of having to listen to Daniel being lauded in
public enough to make her feel nauseous.

'This morning. Caught an earlier flight,' Daniel informed her laconically. 'From Perth,' he added deliberately.

The knowledge that he had guessed at her earlier thoughts with unerring accuracy didn't disconcert Katherine in the slightest. On the contrary, she was glad that Daniel was aware of just how little interest she took in both him and his career.

Fame and fortune hadn't improved his dress sense, she observed disdainfully, assessing the faded denims clinging to the lean hips, and the crumpled blue shirt. Did he deliberately leave his shirt half unbuttoned? she wondered witheringly, encountering the expanse of tanned male skin. The thick, unruly russet hair could do with professional attention, and there was at least two days' growth of beard around the square jawline, the stubble as dark as his eyebrows and lashes.

Nothing had changed, she admitted. She only had to look at Daniel, be in the same room as him for a few minutes, and she felt the familiar surge of antipathy. If James had been her childhood ally and friend, ever since she'd been old enough to be aware of him Daniel, eight years her senior, had been her tormenting adversary. It was as if the Sinclair brothers were the opposite ends of a powerful magnet; she was irresistibly drawn to one and instinctively repelled by the other. Everything about Daniel grated on her: his raw masculinity, his arrogant, unassailable confidence, his lazy, gold-flecked lion's eyes with their habitual expression of cynical amusement as if he regarded the world and its inhabitants as some huge private joke.

The golden boy of the Sinclair family, the favoured son. From a distance, Katherine had witnessed his effortless transition from boyhood to manhood, untouched by the adolescent insecurities that had later plagued both herself and James. Not only academically successful, he'd also been an outstanding athlete and, until an injury to his right leg when he was eighteen had ruled out the possibility of ever reaching the top, had considered becoming a professional sportsman. Fiercely loyal to James, Katherine had always resented the way that he'd been overshadowed by Daniel and been utterly mystified that he not only never appeared to share her resentment but, conversely, had for a long time actually hero-worshipped his elder brother.

Suddenly conscious of the silence not only in the room but in the house, Katherine frowned. 'Isn't James here?'

'No.'

'Do you know when he'll be back?' she demanded with exasperation.

'No idea.' Daniel crossed the green carpet to the sideboard, on which was displayed a bottle of duty-free spirit. 'Haven't seen him since I arrived.'

'How did you get in, then?' Katherine asked suspiciously, beginning to fidget in her chair. He could have told her immediately he'd opened the door that James wasn't at home, she thought irritably. If she'd realised that Daniel was on his own and she was going to be subjected to his undiluted company she would have never entered the cottage.

'The larder window was open. James really ought to be more security conscious,' he added thoughtfully.

Katherine eyed the broad back. How typical of Daniel not only to arrive earlier than expected, but also to make such an unorthodox entry into his brother's home. Acquainted with the size of the window in question, she was slightly amazed that he had managed to engineer his long, muscular frame through its limited confines.

'Drink?' He flicked a glance at her over his shoulder.

'No, thank you,' she replied frigidly, watching as he poured a measure of whisky into a tumbler. Neat whisky at five in the afternoon? 'Late lunch or early supper?' she enquired sweetly.

The tawny golden eyes swept over her and he raised his glass in a mocking salute. 'To my brother and my warm, charming future sister-in-law.'

It hadn't taken him long to get the knives out, Katherine thought bitterly, and then with growing horror the full implication of his words hit her. He wasn't simply taunting her. He genuinely thought... Her expression of polite ennui didn't alter, her eyes didn't drop even for a second from his face.

'To James and Robyn,' she endorsed his toast equably.

Black eyebrows knitted together. 'Who the hell is Robyn?'

'Your warm, charming future sister-in-law,' Katherine said calmly. Why had it been left to her to tell him all this? 'She's a New Zealander and came over to England on a working holiday,' she continued with determined casualness. 'James met her just after Christmas when she was temping in his office.'

If only circumstances had been different, Katherine thought wryly, she would have obtained considerable satisfaction to know that she'd managed to throw Daniel completely off balance. Hope it chokes him, she mused kindly as she watched him toss back the contents of his glass in one gulp.

'I don't believe it! When James called me up in the middle of the night and asked me to be best man I just assumed... And you say he's only known Robyn a few months...' The corners of the firm, straight mouth twitched and then, as if unable to contain his mirth any longer, Daniel threw back his head and roared with laughter, his teeth white against his tanned face. 'After all these years, you've been pipped at the post by a rank outsider!'

'Don't be ridiculous! James and I have never been anything but friends.'

'So that's the official line, is it?' The golden eyes glinted. 'You may have fooled everyone else, but it won't wash with me, Katherine,' he murmured softly.

With detached curiosity Katherine observed the way her hands were entwined together in her lap and wondered vaguely if she'd ever manage to disentangle her numb, frozen fingers. Over the past few months she'd forced herself to acknowledge the agonising truth, and admit that she'd spent her entire adult life loving a man who had never reciprocated her love, who had never regarded her with anything more than brotherly affection, who had been unfailingly kind to her over the last few difficult years simply because kindness was an inherent part of his character. One of the hardest things to accept was that she could have been such a fool, to have seriously imagined that if she were patient, and waited long enough, James would eventually return her feelings, would one day in a blinding flash of self-revelation finally recognise that his childhood friend was the woman he loved. The only consolation was that no one, especially not James, had been aware of the immature daydreams that should have been lain to rest years ago. So at least when he'd announced his engagement to another girl she hadn't been subjected to any sympathetic, knowing glances. Her humiliation and misery had been private. Until now. Slowly she raised her head and looked at Daniel but could learn nothing from his bland, impassive expression. Did he really know what a fool she'd been, or was it simply a shot in the dark?

'Don't look so agitated, Katherine,' he drawled, sitting down in an armchair, stretching his long legs out in front of him. 'I'm not going to make a public announcement. I wouldn't burden James with the guilt.'

No, Katherine thought bitterly. He'd merely use the knowledge to taunt her in private at every opportunity, relish in extracting every ounce of sadistic enjoyment from the situation. Then with sudden insight she realised that she could bear any amount of verbal taunts from him. It would have been his pity that she would have found unendurable.

'You should have seduced James years ago,' he murmured as casually as if they were discussing the weather. 'Scrapped the sensible, capable girl-next-door routine. That was the fatal mistake in your strategy. You should have used your body, not waited for James to fall in love with your beautiful character.'

Katherine smiled. It would take a lot more than that to make her lose her temper. 'Tips from the master?' she enquired sweetly. Why did she find the suggestion that she should have virtually lured James to her bed less offensive than being described as sensible? 'I was forgetting what an expert you are on relationships.' She paused and frowned thoughtfully. 'How long did your marriage last? Three months, or was it four?'

She saw the muscles tense along his jaw and for a brief second was ashamed of her vindictive thrust, wondering what drove her and Daniel to seek out each other's wounds and rub salt in them. His marriage must have been the first time in his life he'd encountered failure, she realised. How had he dealt with it? Had he suffered? Was he still suffering? Compassion stirred inside her and was ruthlessly squashed. She wasn't going to waste any sympathy on Daniel. The day his Canadian wife had walked out of their Toronto home he'd probably gone out to the nearest bar, drunk himself into oblivion, woken the next morning with thumping hangover, shrugged off the past and carried on with the rest of his life.

'So why exactly have you come to see James? Some last-ditch attempt to dissuade him from the forthcoming nuptials?'

Katherine flicked a glance across the room, distaste clouding her green eyes as they moved over the indolent form and came to rest on the mocking face. 'My van's broken down. I was hoping James might have a look at it.'

Daniel raised a dark eyebrow. 'Have Tarrants closed down, then?' he asked with interest.

Katherine didn't answer but rose abruptly to her feet and picked up her jacket. Daniel was getting uncomfortably near the truth. She shouldn't have come here today, shouldn't have given in to that overwhelming longing to see James just once more on his own before Saturday. The van had simply been a heaven-sent excuse to justify her unexpected visit. She'd even had to walk past the local garage, to which Daniel had referred, to reach the cottage.

'You've got to let him go, Katherine.'

In the process of tugging on her jacket, Katherine paused, taken aback by the uncharacteristic seriousness not only in the deep voice but in the tawny eyes that drew and held hers. No hint of mockery or derision in those golden depths, but something less tangible and infinitely more disturbing. Concern? Sympathy? Understanding? Her mouth tightened. She didn't want any of those things from Daniel. She jerked her eyes from his face as she heard the front door slam shut and the sound of approaching footsteps.

'I'd hate to cramp your style,' Daniel drawled. He unfolded his long body and stood up. 'Want me to beat a hasty, tactful retreat?'

Katherine flicked him a glance, recognised the familiar, caustic twist of his mouth, the sardonic gleam in his eyes, and was oddly relieved to know that the status quo had returned to normal. 'I believe the Sahara is very pleasant at this time of the year,' she murmured politely, and smiled casually as James entered the room.

'Katherine! Haven't see you for weeks.' Evincing no surprise at her presence in his home, he kissed her lightly on the cheek. It was the briefest of salutations, one that James might have bestowed on any of his female relatives, and normally Katherine would have received it with equanimity. But today, aware of her silent observer, she felt self-conscious and awkward, and was relieved when James's attention focused on Daniel, giving her a moment's respite to recollect herself.

'How's everything?'

'Fine. And you?'

Despite her tension, Katherine's wide mouth curved in amusement as she listened to the laconic exchange between the two men, who were acting as if it were days rather than years since they'd last met. James looked absurdly happy, she registered with a twist of her heart. Kind, unassuming, gentle James, he was the complete antithesis of his elder brother in character, and, with his rich copper hair and warm brown eyes, by far the better looking. Classically handsome, his fine, sculptured features were smooth and regular, whereas Daniel's face looked as if it had been chiselled out of hard, unyielding rock by a none too gentle hand. Katherine's eyes flickered from one man to another, comparing them as she'd been comparing them for as long as she could remember, aware from the quizzical lift of Daniel's eyebrow as he glanced at her from over James's shoulder that he was perfectly aware of both her assessment and her verdict, and was amused by it.

'I was going to telephone you tomorrow, Kat.' James turned to face her. 'Dad's made me a partner as a wedding present.'

'Congratulations,' Daniel drawled, clasping his brother's shoulder.

'That's wonderful news,' Katherine murmured but couldn't inject as much enthusiasm into her voice as she would have liked, and for the first time in her life, as she looked at James's jubilant expression, she felt a surge of deep irritation. How could he be so totally insensitive as to have never suspected for a moment how she felt about him? Had he never once stopped to wonder why she'd spent so much of her precious free time helping him renovate the cottage and working on his garden? Had he genuinely believed that she'd been motivated purely by friendship and a wish to repay his kindness over the van? As careful as she'd been to guard her feelings over the years, surely there must have been times that she'd betrayed herself...? And now here he was, expecting her to be totally altruistic and rejoice in his happiness with another girl. She wasn't going to mention the van, she suddenly decided. She'd leave now and go straight to the garage, where she should have gone in the first place.

'Good heavens, is that the time?' she murmured, glancing at her wrist-watch with a frown. 'I didn't re-alise it was so late. I really must dash, James. I just popped in to wish you luck for Saturday,' she added lightly, not daring to glance at Daniel.

'Thanks,' James smiled down at her, not seeming the least perturbed by her abrupt departure only minutes after he himself had arrived, evidently completely satisfied by her explanation.

'What about the van?' Daniel enquired blandly as she began to move towards the door, and she cursed him silently.

'Oh, lord, has it broken down again?' James asked immediately, and as she saw the concern flooding his dark eyes Katherine felt ashamed of her earlier irritation. There would never be a man to equal him, she acknowledged, swallowing hard. He was quite simply the kindest, most considerate person she'd ever known.

'I'm supposed to be picking Robyn up in half an hour, and driving to Heathrow to meet her family,' he continued anxiously. 'I won't have time to look at it until tomorrow.'

'Is the Land Rover still on the road?' Daniel drawled, crossing the room.

His brother nodded. 'Yes, and there's a tool kit and jump leads in the back.'

'OK. Ready, Katherine?'

She glanced at Daniel speculatively. Was she to assume that he was offering his services as mechanic? 'There's really no need,' she began ungraciously and then closed her mouth, common sense warring with pride and winning. Daniel was the last person in the world from whom she'd normally seek or accept assistance but, regardless of whether he was able to repair the van or not, she would be grateful for a lift home, she admitted, the alternative being a three-hour wait for the next country bus or an eight-mile walk in the rain.

She followed him into the hall, waiting while he pulled a waxed jacket, borrowed from James, over his shirt. She'd always supposed the two men to be of a similar build, yet the jacket, which fitted James perfectly, was stretched tautly across the breadth of Daniel's shoulders.

She zipped up her own jacket as she stepped out of the front door and then paused for a moment, turning round to survey the cottage. A chapter of her life was closing. She would never come here again without a formal invitation from both James and Robyn—perhaps not even then. The days when she casually dropped in on James for a cup of tea and a chat whenever she felt like it were gone forever. A great wave of sadness and loneliness swamped over her. She felt as if she weren't just losing the man she loved but also her oldest friend.

Abruptly she turned her back on the cottage, and walked over to the Land Rover, her eyes narrowing against the rain that showed no sign of abating. She opened the passenger door and Daniel leaned over from the driver's seat and held out a helping hand. She grasped it without thinking, surprised to discover how instantly aware she was of the strong, warm fingers curled around hers.

He made no effort to release her hand as she clambered up beside him but, his eyebrows drawn together in a black line across his forehead, surveyed her torn, ragged nails and the callouses on the palm of her hand where blisters had turned to hard skin.

'I became bored doing TV commercials for nail polish,' Katherine muttered, snatching her hand away and hiding it in the pocket of her jacket. She was a gardener, not a model! Did Daniel think she had nothing better to do with her time than sit around all day, manicuring her nails? She was being abnormally sensitive, she admitted, but her ego and confidence had taken a dive since James's engagement, and the slightest implied personal criticism caught her on the raw.

'Don't you wear gloves?' Daniel started up the engine, switched on the windscreen wipers, and the Land Rover moved smoothly down the drive and into the road.

'Sometimes.' She shrugged. The state of her hands was hardly the most riveting of conversational topics and she wondered why he was bothering to pursue it.

'Is Jack Mathews still working part-time for you?'

'No,' Katherine said regretfully. 'His wife died a year ago and he moved down to Sussex to live with his daughter.' It was the advice and enthusiasm of the elderly, experienced gardener, rather than his practical help, that she missed most.

'So you're running the market garden entirely on your own now?'

'I have a couple of students who help out at weekends and during the vacations.' Katherine let her eyes flicker over the hard planes of his face, surprised and slightly suspicious of his apparent quite genuine interest. In the past, she recalled, he'd always been scathing about the market garden. He'd refused to acknowledge it as a serious business venture, had with irritating regularity referred to it condescendingly as her hobby, implying that it was merely something to keep her occupied while the twins were at school.

'You ought to employ a full-time assistant, someone who could take over the heavier work,' Daniel murmured idly.

Katherine eyes darkened with exasperation. Same old chauvinist, she thought acidly, handing out free, un-asked-for advice. Her profit margin wasn't sufficient as yet to justify paying out wages for full-time staff. But, having no inclination to reveal the financial state of her business, she ignored his remark and gazed fixedly out of the window as they drove into the market square and drew up alongside the easily identifiable van.

Fluorescent lime-green letters on the side of the van proclaimed the nature of the produce being transported inside, and, to eliminate any remaining doubt, a selection of large, dazzling pink vegetables were portrayed beneath the lettering.

'The twins did it about a year ago,' Katherine explained casually, seeing Daniel's raised eyebrows. 'They were bored one weekend and decided to give in to their creative urges.' The result had been somewhat alarming but she hadn't been unduly concerned. She felt no affection for the van, had never been inclined to form sentimental attachments to inanimate objects. Even as a child, she'd been more interested in the living.

She opened the door and was just about to leap out when Daniel put a restraining hand on her shoulder. 'You might as well stay here. There's no point in us both getting soaked.'

Moving forward slightly, so that his arm fell from her shoulder, Katherine looked at him thoughtfully. She would have expected such consideration from James, but never from Daniel. This was the second time in barely five minutes that he had shown an uncharacteristic interest in her welfare, she realised, oddly disturbed by the knowledge. 'So what's prompted this sudden rush of brotherly concern for me?' she enquired, distrusting him completely.

His mouth curved mockingly. 'Don't ever make the mistake of confusing me with James, sweetheart,' he drawled, turning round to retrieve the tool kit from the back of the Land Rover.

'I hardly think I'm in any danger of doing that,' Katherine scoffed, wondering why the casual remark had sounded almost like a threat. Sweetheart, indeed, she thought scathingly. He sounded like a gangster from an old Hollywood B movie.

'Keys?' He quirked a dark eyebrow at her.

'Here you are, honey,' she smiled, producing them from her pocket.

'Thanks, doll,' he said, straight-faced, and despite herself Katherine grinned. He'd always had the uncanny and disconcerting ability of sensing her thoughts. It was something that she would have to watch.

The tool kit in his hand, he jumped down from the Land Rover and strode over to the van, his movements fluid and controlled. It was odd, Katherine reflected, that, despite their mutual antipathy, in some respects she felt more at ease in Daniel's company than James's. It was probably because she never cared what he thought of her, never had to watch what she said or did, his caustic comments normally leaving her unmoved. Whereas with James there was always that constant fear that she might give herself away.

Perhaps she should have been more honest with James a long time ago, and openly admitted her feelings. The end result would have probably been the same, she admitted, and she would also have probably lost him as a friend, but at least she would have been spared wasting so many years living in false hope.

A surge of depression swamped her and she leaned back in her seat, her eyes resting on the lean figure bending over the open bonnet of the van but no longer registering him. Why couldn't James have fallen in love with her? she thought drearily. It would have made life so simple. The twins got on exceptionally well with him—

there would have been no problems on that front—and she knew his mother had always been fond of her, regarding her almost as the daughter she'd never had.

'You've got to let him go.' Daniel's words reverberated through her head and she closed her eyes, screwing them up tightly, her hands forming tightly clenched fists in her lap. Daniel was right. She had to stop thinking about James and get on with the rest of her life. And meet other men? Was that what she meant? Even if the thought hadn't been singularly unappealing, she didn't have a clue of how to go about that anyway. Gardening was essentially a lonely occupation, and except for market day she had little contact with the general public. The only young men of her acquaintance were those with whom she'd been at school and college. She'd dated some of them briefly over the years, had enjoyed their company, but had retreated immediately they had suggested a deeper involvement. So what did she do to widen her limited horizon? Get dressed up to the nines and go to a nightclub with the express purpose of searching for a man? The thought made her shudder with revulsion. Quite frankly, she admitted, she didn't want a man in her life unless it was James, and neither did she ever want to risk falling in love again. Perhaps one day she might change her mind, might meet someone who could match up to James—he would always be the yardstick by which she measured other men—but until that unlikely day dawned she would concentrate all her energies on the market garden and the twins. She heaved a deep sigh, her shoulders sagging with despondency, the future suddenly appearing unbelievably bleak. 'Oh, James,' she half muttered under her breath.

'Do you need the van in the morning?'

She swept open her eyes, disconcerted to see Daniel standing by the open window, watching her with narrowed eyes. Rivulets of water poured down his jacket and his hair, darkened by the rain to a rich, deep brown, was plastered to his head.

'No,' she said swiftly. Her thrice-weekly, early-morning deliveries to the local farm shop and greengrocer who sold her produce were made on Mondays, Thursdays and Saturdays.

'Right. In that case, I'll jump start it and drive it back to James's. You can take the Land Rover home,' he said curtly.

'Thank you,' she said stiffly, registering the brusqueness in his voice and the grim lines drawn around his straight mouth. There had been no need for him to sound so ungracious. Admittedly he was soaked to the skin, and probably suffering from jet lag, but she hadn't asked him for assistance, he had offered it. 'What's the matter with the van?' she asked hesitantly.

'Alternator. I'll replace it tomorrow and bring the van over.' Turning away abruptly, he walked to the back of the Land Rover to retrieve the jump leads.

Katherine frowned. Why was he helping her like this? He could just as easily have suggested taking the van to the garage. It wasn't as if she was some helpless, eyelash-fluttering, ultra-feminine type who instinctively inspired male chivalry. Ever since her parents' death she'd deliberately contrived to give the impression of being completely self-sufficient, capable of dealing with any situation that came her way, deciding that it was the only way of making Jesse and Tim feel completely secure in her guardianship. Even James had accepted the façade, had no idea of just how much she secretly relied on his support. Perhaps that was hardly surprising—she was

fast coming to the conclusion that James accepted
everyone completely at face value. Sometimes she felt
as if she spent her entire life acting out various parts—
the role of calm, dependable big sister to the twins, loyal,
platonic friend to James, reliable, efficient business-
woman to those to whom she sold her produce. She
grinned wryly. All the adjectives made her sound so
worthy—and about as inspiring as a supermarket trolley.
She was definitely lacking in the fascinating *femme fatale*
department these days!

The grin vanished from her face, her whole body
tensing as she watched Daniel walk back across to the
van. He wasn't moving with his usual, long, easy loping
strides, but limping, favouring his right leg.

He was probably exhausted after the long flight from
Australia. The barely perceptible limp, the residue of
the old leg injury, was always the tell-tale sign. Was he
in pain? she wondered uneasily. Did that explain the
tightness around his mouth? He was standing in front
of the van now, attaching the jump leads to the battery,
his stance stiff and awkward, his weight balanced
unevenly.

Abruptly Katherine turned her eyes away, finding she
couldn't bear to watch him any longer. Stop feeling
guilty, she ordered herself harshly. You were only ten
years old... it was an accident... But it was no good.
She felt the familiar, knotted, twisted sensation crawl
over her and begin to gnaw deep inside her. Would she
ever be free of the guilt, of Daniel? And would he ever
forgive her?

CHAPTER TWO

IF ONLY Katherine could actually remember what had happened that summer's afternoon thirteen years ago—the year Daniel had qualified for the Wimbledon Lawn Tennis Championships. But her recollections were so hazy, little more than disjointed fragments...

Cycling along the gravel farm track beside James on the new bicycle she'd received for her tenth birthday, supervised from behind by a lofty eighteen-year-old Daniel. Stopping to let a tractor reverse out of a field gate. A small brown and white dog appeared from no-where, running across the track, oblivious to the danger of the large moving vehicle... At that point her memory seemed to stop functioning. Blank. Then the remainder of the school term, spent with her arm in a sling; Daniel in hospital for weeks, later on hobbling about on crutches, Wimbledon an abandoned dream.

It was James, the only witness to the accident, who had a long time later filled in the gaps her memory had conveniently blotted out.

'You thought the dog was going to be run over,' he'd told her quietly. She'd flung her bike aside and sped on short sturdy legs towards the tractor. The driver, concentrating on his manoeuvre, hadn't seen her, hadn't expected a child to be running towards him... The dog had been unhurt, and she'd received relatively minor injuries—a broken arm, a few scratches... Daniel, who had snatched her out of the way of those huge, rolling tyres, had had his right leg crushed.

'Anything you need from the van?'

Katherine looked at Daniel blankly and then nodded. She leapt down from the Land Rover, walked swiftly to the rear of the van and extracted the crate containing the unsold produce. Silently Daniel took it from her arms and deposited it in the Land Rover.

'I'll disconnect the jump leads when you start up the van,' she offered in a subdued voice, looking up at him. 'And thanks.' Thanks for helping her with the van? Or thanks for saving her life all those years ago? Even if she hadn't been killed, she would have doubtlessly suffered serious multiple injuries, might have been crippled. They'd never talked about the accident. Every time she'd tentatively broached the subject Daniel had turned his back on her, had rebuffed her awkward attempts to express her gratitude and sympathy. For a long time she'd sensed that he couldn't bear to be in the same room as her, couldn't stand to even look at her. She'd seen the accusatory expression in his eyes, had known that he blamed her for wrecking his tennis career. It hadn't been fair to burden her with that lifelong guilt, the adult Katherine protested vehemently. She'd only been ten years old ...

The golden gaze swept over her face. 'See you tomorrow, Katherine.'

'Yes,' she murmured, registering vaguely that it had stopped raining. She remained motionless as Daniel bent his head towards her, steeling herself to receive the light kiss he usually bestowed on her cheek whenever they parted company. She was fully aware that he did it to annoy her and she had long ago decided that the best policy was simply to ignore the unwanted but mercifully brief caress. It was a stupid, ridiculous game that they had been playing since her late teens.

She felt the fleeting touch of his lips against her cheek, was about to turn away, when a strong hand clamped down on her shoulder and swung her back around. Instantly mistrustful, she looked up at Daniel and saw the golden glint in his eyes as they rested thoughtfully on her mouth. She swallowed down the illogical surge of panic. He wouldn't dare! He was simply trying to wind her up, that was all.

Slowly and deliberately he bent his head towards her again. Katherine, still convinced that he was merely tormenting her, stood her ground, and was caught totally off guard as he carried out his wordless threat and the warm, firm mouth covered hers.

Her instinct was to recoil, jerk her head backwards, push him away with all her force. Instead, she remained completely impassive, her eyes wide open, refusing even to acknowledge the expert lips moving lingeringly over hers, the hands tightening around her waist. He was trying to evoke some sort of reaction from her and she wasn't going to fall into the trap, wasn't going to give him the satisfaction of displaying any emotion at all.

'When you're ready I'll start up the engine,' she said coolly as he lifted his head, and, turning away, clambered up into the Land Rover. It wasn't until she tried to turn the ignition key that she realised that she was trembling, and a quick, cursory glance in the driving mirror confirmed her suspicion that her cheeks were flushed and her eyes over-bright.

She was nearly home, driving along the familiar, narrow lane, skirted by fields, before she finally admitted the uncomfortable truth. For a moment, trapped in Daniel's arms, she'd found some part of her wanting to respond to that firm, persuasive mouth, to close her eyes, and submerge herself completely in the warm pleasure that had beckoned so tantalisingly, just out of reach. It would be easy to claim that, in her present emotionally vulnerable state, she'd become momentarily confused, had wishfully imagined that it was James kissing her, holding her, that she'd nearly succumbed to a fantasy. But it wouldn't be true. Her eyes had been wide open. She'd been wholly conscious that it was Daniel's powerful arms around her, that it was his hard mouth teasing her senses until she was a hair's breadth from capitulation. She grimaced, imagining all too vividly the triumphant mockery in his eyes if she had done so. How could she have felt even the briefest transitory spark of physical attraction for a man whom she'd always rejected mentally, and who returned her aversion? Especially when she was in love with that man's brother. She grinned a little self-consciously. Wasn't she rather over-reacting, and thereby playing right into Daniel's hands? OK, so he had kissed her and it hadn't been as unpleasant as she would have preferred, but she wasn't going to lose any sleep over it. She'd already wasted enough of that precious commodity over James.

She glanced left automatically as she passed a pair of ornate wrought-iron gates that guarded a long tree-lined avenue leading up to Norrington Hall. The last member of the Norrington family had died intestate, since which time the eighteenth-century house had passed through a succession of hands. It had been purchased by a property dealer who had totally underestimated the strength of local feeling to his proposal to demolish, in his view, the antiquated and impractical mansion and replace it with a dozen modern dwellings. His planning permission had been turned down and the house sold to an American, who had restored it with painstaking care. Unfortunately, after enduring three dank grey English winters, his wife had persuaded him to return to their native Florida, and the beautiful old house was once again on the market.

The twins had left the gate open for her, and Katherine swung the Land Rover up the drive and parked in front of the red-bricked thatched house in which she'd lived all her life. Set in a two-acre plot of land adjoining Norrington Hall, bordered on three sides by parkland, and on the fourth by woodland, the six-bedroomed house was too large for herself and the twins, and she'd contemplated moving to a smaller one after her parents' death, but had finally decided that the twins had suffered enough trauma already without having to leave their familiar home surroundings. Fortunately, due to her father's substantial life-insurance policy, there had been no immediate financial pressure to sell the house. A trust fund had been set up for the twins' education; the majority of the remaining capital had been invested to provide a small but adequate regular income for day to day household expenditure, leaving a small residue which Katherine had used to finance her small enterprise.

Jumping out of the Land Rover, she walked down the drive to close the gate, glancing up warily into the foliage of the oak tree that had withstood the storms of recent years. A large ginger tom-cat had lately taken to performing the death-defying trick of leaping out of the seemingly innocent branches on to any moving target that took its fancy. And, for some perverse reason, Katherine seemed to be the favoured victim of its surprise attacks, which she deemed grossly unfair, as she had been the one to discover and take pity on the thin, half-grown cat that had arrived on their doorstep a year ago.

'I should have let you starve,' she muttered severely as she spotted Thomas's amber eyes peering down at her

malevolently, and, closing the gate, walked swiftly round
to the back of the house, entering the kitchen.

'Just in time,' Jessica greeted her cheerfully, gyrating
in time to the loud music issuing from the portable radio
perched up on the oak dresser as she set the round
wooden table for supper. 'Did James fix the van?'

'Daniel's going to mend it tomorrow.' Katherine hung
up her damp jacket behind the back door.

'Oh, I wish I'd known Daniel was back. I would have
come with you. Has he changed at all, or is he still the
same gorgeous hunk?' Jessica demanded enthusiastically, and, looking up at her sister, added with a frown,
'What's the matter with your face? It looks as if you've
got some sort of rash.'

'It does feel a bit itchy,' Katherine admitted, glad to
dodge the first question, still shuddering from Jessica's
description of Daniel. She'd never understood her
younger sister's schoolgirl crush on him. 'I'll go and have
a quick wash.' She walked across the red-tiled kitchen
floor and out into the hall.

The door of the downstairs cloakroom was closed and
she suppressed a grin as she heard the faint whirring
sound issuing from within, recognising the noise as that
of the electric shaver she'd bought for Tim last
Christmas, having begun to notice the soft down on his
chin.

The door opened and Tim emerged, rubbing a hand
over his pink, shining jaw in a wholly masculine gesture.
'Saves shaving in the morning,' he informed her loftily.

'Yes,' Katherine agreed gravely, lowering her eyes so
that he wouldn't see her amusement, and closed the
cloakroom door behind her.

Running water into the white basin, she surveyed her
reflection in the mirror above it, momentarily puzzled

by the livid red blotches around her mouth and chin. Then, as her eyes alighted on Tim's razor, realisation dawned... Daniel's stubble, as abrasive as sandpaper against her sensitive skin... Scowling ferociously, cursing him soundly under her breath, Katherine splashed water on her face.

After washing up the supper dishes, Katherine left the twins poring over textbooks in the living-room, not entirely convinced by their argument that loud, discordant background music was conducive to study, and went out into the plot of land at the rear of the house which was now given up completely to the cultivation of vegetables.

Walking down the path towards the greenhouse, she felt a twinge of nostalgia as she recalled the gracious, sweeping lawns of her childhood, and the grass tennis court where her father had taught her the rudiments of the game. She wondered if she'd ever be able to think of her parents without that tearing jolt of pain. Another memory stirred, a new, unwanted image filling her head. Herself shortly before her tenth birthday, long corn-coloured plaits tumbling over her shoulders as, with a tennis racket gripped firmly in both hands, she tried determinedly to return the balls being tossed to her over the net by a tall boy with russet hair and teasing tawny-golden eyes. Not a boy, she amended quickly, but a man. A man with strong, powerful legs, whom the sporting Press had enthusiastically proclaimed to be the most promising English tennis player for generations. That afternoon had been the last time she could ever recall seeing a tennis racket in Daniel's hand, yet until then it had seemed like a permanent appendage. Her throat tightened. All those hours and hours of practice Daniel had put in...all that potential never realised...all those dreams and ambitions shattered...

Ferociously Katherine kicked a pebble from the path. Why the hell did Daniel have to start limping while she was watching? She filled up a watering-can from the water butt and entered the greenhouse.

It was nearly dusk when she'd finished her outdoor chores and, returning to the kitchen, she settled down wearily at the table, spreading books around her, and started to update her business accounts, her least favourite task.

This was the first year that she was starting to show a profit, although it was hardly one that reflected the long, arduous hours she worked. She would never have entertained the idea of starting up her own business had her father not left his family financially secure, she admitted. To make the market garden a really viable concern she needed to expand. Needed more land and to invest in modern, expensive labour-saving machinery. Sighing, she chewed the top of her pen. She'd never been overtly ambitious. Feeble as it undoubtedly sounded, all she'd ever wanted to do was marry James and have his children. It would have been so safe, so comfortable. A dark cloud of depression hovered over her head and she fought it off determinedly. Sometimes she half wished she'd been jilted by James, or at least had an affair with him. Then at least she'd have some justification for feeling so damn miserable. Behaving like a lovelorn adolescent over a man with whom she'd never had more than a platonic relationship was so...

She unclenched her hands quickly, and bowed her head over a sheet of paper as the twins trooped into the kitchen, announcing that they were suffering from acute hunger pangs that could only be assuaged by chocolate biscuits.

'There's plenty of fruit in the bowl. Have an orange or an apple,' Katherine offered unsympathetically, and then relented. 'OK, but only two biscuits each.' She glanced up at her younger sister and added casually, 'May I borrow that manicure set you had last Christmas, Jesse? Oh, and some hand-cream? I've run out.'

'Course. Help yourself. It's on my dressing-table.'

When the twins reappeared in the kitchen some time later to bid their elder sister goodnight they found her sitting with an oddly thoughtful expression on her face, massaging cream into her hands.

Katherine failed to hear the alarm clock the following morning and woke with a headache, something she rarely suffered from. She'd slept badly, disturbed by images of James, superimposed on for some reason by those of his brother. Feeling utterly disgruntled, wishing both Sinclair men on another planet, albeit for different reasons, she washed hastily, pulled on a pair of faded jeans and a checked cotton shirt passed on to her by Tim, and made her way downstairs to the kitchen.

Tim was wandering around, eating burnt toast, oblivious to the trail of crumbs behind him. Dirty knives lay scattered over every conceivable surface. Why, Katherine wondered, did her brother feel compelled to use a clean knife to spread each slice of toast, and was he unaware that there was a washing-up bowl in the kitchen? Jessica was apparently engaged in conversation with a plate of cereal, the gist of the monologue being that it was completely futile and an utter waste of time to go to school to sit a French exam she had no hope of passing.

The ginger tom was battering against the kitchen window, vociferously demanding breakfast, and when

Katherine obediently produced a laden bowl she was reprimanded for her tardiness by a swift, recalcitrant paw.

'Vicious brute!' To compound matters, Katherine then cut the tip of her right thumb as she replaced the lid on the tin of cat food.

Tim immediately downed toast, and insisted on attending to her feline-related injuries, disinfecting them and carefully applying a plaster to her thumb.

'I thought you wanted to be a vet, not a doctor,' Katherine muttered ungratefully, one vigilant eye on the wall clock, having the distinct feeling that Tim rather regretted that her wounds hadn't been more severe.

After depositing the twins at the bus stop in the Land Rover, she returned to the house, swallowed a couple of aspirins to ease her throbbing head, and swiftly dispensed with the household chores.

Swapping her light sandals for her sturdy gardening boots, she covered her face liberally with the total sunblock cream she used as a protective skin barrier most of the year round and stepped out into the garden, her spirits rising a notch as she gazed up at the cloudless azure sky. She tugged on her thick gardening gloves and, armed with a hoe, settled to her first task of the day, earthing up the potatoes, drawing the soil up around the shoots.

Her mood of temporary well-being began to fade as the morning wore on. The cut on her thumb throbbed with an intensity that bore no relation to its severity every time she put any pressure on it, and hampered her progress. By lunchtime she was behind the schedule she'd mentally prepared for the morning and felt an unfamiliar swell of panic curdling up inside her. There simply weren't enough hours in the day to complete all the tasks that needed attending to. She straightened up, lifting the mane of thick hair from her damp neck, and looked around her dejectedly. Why didn't she give up the market garden? Now the twins were older, there was nothing to stop her seeking full-time employment at a local nursery or even returning to college to complete her course. She tugged off her gloves, saw the crimson-stained plaster on her thumb and burst into tears. For heaven's sake, surely she wasn't crying over a tiny cut on her thumb? This propensity to keep bursting into tears at the slightest provocation really had to stop. Disgustedly she dashed the tears from her eyes and marched up towards the house.

She kicked off her thick, cumbersome gardening boots and padded upstairs to wash and exchange her sticky jeans and shirt for a pair of cotton shorts and a T-shirt. Feeling considerably cooler, she returned to the kitchen, switched on the electric kettle and retrieved a wholemeal loaf from the bread bin.

'Brought the van back,' a voice drawled laconically from behind her, and she swung round and saw Daniel looming in the open doorway. Dressed with his usual casualness in denims and an open-necked shirt, he was clean shaven today, the cleft in the square, tenacious chin no longer concealed by dark stubble.

'Thank you.' Katherine crossed the tiled floor to the open brick fireplace. 'I'll get the Land Rover keys.' She reached up and collected them from a jug on top of the mantelpiece and, aware of just how ungracious she sounded, sighed inwardly, adding reluctantly, 'I was just about to make a sandwich. Would you like one?'

She hoped he would refuse, but he accepted her offer with alacrity and sat down on a wooden stool, stretching out his legs in front of him. Out of the corner of her eye she saw the ginger cat saunter into the kitchen, tail raised in a question mark. Slightly bemused, she watched as it leapt on to Daniel's knee, head-butted his chin affectionately and curled up on his lap, purring ferociously.

Traitor, Katherine thought silently, encountering a pair of unblinking, complacent amber eyes, and, turning her back, started to prepare two cheese and lettuce sandwiches. She switched on the kettle again and glanced over her shoulder.

'Tea, or would you prefer a cold drink?'

'Tea, please.'

Daniel was quite blatantly studying her long, suntanned legs, but the appreciation in his eyes didn't fool Katherine for a moment. It was faked, a deliberate ruse to make her feel self-conscious and awkward, and it wasn't going to work. She was perfectly aware that she had never attracted Daniel physically. She wasn't his type. Judging from the women she'd seen in his company over the years, he had a penchant for petite brunettes with large, sultry brown eyes, and fortunately she didn't qualify on any of those counts. Tall green-eyed blondes with hands like sandpaper were quite evidently not to his taste. Nor, she reminded herself with a twist of her heart, did they appear to be to James's, either. Although quite frankly she doubted whether James even saw her as a female any more. 'You should have seduced James years ago.' Unbidden, Daniel's words crept into her head. She wouldn't even know how to go about seducing James, or anyone else, for that matter, even had she wanted to. At twenty-three, her experience with men was severely limited—a few goodnight kisses that hadn't had any discernible effect on her pulse-rate and that was about it. Hardly the stuff to make the front page of the more sensational of the tabloids.

'Four.'

'What?' Katherine muttered absently, spooning tea into the pot.

'Five.'

She shrugged, closing the lid on the tea caddy before she transferred the entire contents into the pot. She filled up the latter with boiling water, left it to draw and reached up to a shelf for two mugs. One slipped from her fingers and crashed to the floor but miraculously remained intact.

'Pre-wedding nerves?' Daniel enquired conversationally.

Stooping to pick up the mug, Katherine ignored him, but inwardly admitted that, with his habitual perceptiveness, Daniel was uncomfortably close to the truth. As Saturday approached relentlessly she was becoming increasingly tense and edgy. She was sleeping badly, was perpetually tired, and in her state of semi-exhaustion she was becoming irrational, losing all sense of proportion. Even the most trivial of problems was beginning to appear insurmountable.

Katherine poured out two mugs of tea, and placed one on the table in front of Daniel, together with his sandwich. She picked up her own plate and hesitated, curiously loath to sit down beside Daniel. The farmhouse-style kitchen was enormous by modern standards, and yet it suddenly seemed claustrophobic.

'Shall we go and sit in the garden?' she murmured casually, and Daniel tipped the cat gently from his lap and followed her out of the back door.

She collected a rug from the shed and led the way around to the wild, natural garden at the side of the house which she'd deliberately left uncultivated. She spread out the rug in the shade of an old, gnarled apple tree and sat down. She assumed that Daniel would occupy the large space she'd left for him, and was disconcerted when he sat down close beside her, and she felt a hard band of muscle pressing against her right hip. Any closer and he would be sitting in her lap! What on earth was he playing at? she wondered irritably, recoiling inwardly from the physical contact. Ignore him, pretend you haven't even noticed, she ordered herself, gazing blankly ahead as she swiftly drank her tea and then took a bite from her sandwich. But how exactly did she shut her mind off to that oppressively masculine presence beside her? She felt as if every inch of her being was being infiltrated by some intangible force.

'Did you grow the lettuce? It's delicious.'

'Yes,' Katherine said shortly. Her sense of smell was dominated by the tang of male aftershave mixed with the soapy scent of clean skin. She'd always been aware of Daniel, but in the past it had been as James's brother, as her lifelong antagonist; she'd never been so aware of him before simply as a man.

'Would you like the other half of my sandwich?' She was no longer hungry, hadn't even tasted the crisp, sweet lettuce. Daniel's appetite, she noted, wasn't similarly impaired and he'd already devoured his own sandwich with effortless ease.

'On a diet?' he enquired sympathetically, taking hold of the proffered plate.

'No,' Katherine murmured with a serene smile, watching as he swallowed a mouthful of sandwich. 'I've just remembered that I forgot to wash the lettuce and it's my vegetarian day.' Scrambling to her feet, she picked up the two empty mugs. 'I'll get some more tea.'

She felt much calmer as she entered the cool kitchen, her former agitation now seeming utterly ridiculous. And her appetite seemed to have returned with a vengeance.

She helped herself to a banana from the fruit bowl, then impulsively raced upstairs to her bedroom and stood in front of the full-length mirror, inspecting herself critically from all angles. Was she on a diet? Huh! She might not be in any danger of being blown away by a strong gust of wind, and she didn't have to avoid walking over grids in the pavement, but she most certainly wasn't fat! She gazed at the tall girl with indignant green eyes and grinned. Minor victory to Daniel!

She drank her own tea in the kitchen, reapplied a fresh plaster to her thumb, and then tugged on her thick socks and gardening boots. She picked up her gloves, and carried Daniel's replenished mug back round to the wild garden. She faltered slightly as she saw him lying stretched out on the rug, arms folded behind his head. The sun filtered through the overhead canopy of leaves and glinted on his thick russet hair, igniting it with red flames. His eyes were closed. Asleep or just bluffing? Even in repose, he had a sardonic quirk to his mouth.

'Tea,' she announced briskly, nudging his foot with her shoe.

The tawny-gold eyes flickered open. 'Woken by a kick,' Daniel drawled, easing himself into a sitting position and raking a hand through his unruly hair. He swallowed down his tea and raised a dark eyebrow at her. 'Don't let me detain you,' he said courteously, and with a casual smile flopped back on the rug and closed his eyes.

Katherine surveyed the prone form with exasperation. If Daniel intended to spend the afternoon loafing in the sun, couldn't he at least have selected someone else's garden in which to do so?

'I've an appointment at five. Could you wake me about half-past four?' he murmured indolently. 'Preferably by the more traditional method.'

'Anything else, sir?' Katherine enquired drily, her eyes dropping involuntarily to the firm, straight mouth as she absorbed the full implication of his words. Was he taunting her? she wondered uneasily. Did he know how close she'd come to capitulation yesterday, or was she being overly sensitive, reading too much into the flippant remark?

Daniel raised his head. 'A cushion wouldn't come amiss.'

'Sorry. I'm right out of cushions.' Did he think she had nothing better to do than run around after him all afternoon? 'I'm sure James or your mother have plenty,' she added helpfully, hoping he would take the hint and make a rapid departure.

'Not to worry,' Daniel drawled lazily. Calmly he stripped off his shirt, and folded it to form a makeshift pillow behind his head.

She'd seen Daniel without a shirt on before. The sight of the gleaming bronze shoulders, the deep, powerful chest sprinkled with fine dark hairs, the taut, flat stomach should have left her unmoved. But it didn't. The expanse of smooth golden skin unsettled her, made her feel tense and awkward, as gauche as a teenager. The realisation that she seemed to have lost her ability to view Daniel with complete detachment, that once again some part of her was responding to his blatant masculinity, shook her profoundly.

Abruptly Katherine turned away and marched round to the back garden. The apathy she'd experienced before lunch was dispelled; she felt an edge, keyed up, fired with a restless, frenetic energy. Without pausing for a break, she toiled solidly for the next few hours, planting out marrow and bean plants from the greenhouse into the prepared, well-composted soil. She concentrated solely on the task in hand, refused to let her thoughts wander off at disturbing tangents. She lost all sense of time, was oblivious to the heat, and if her thumb still smarted she no longer felt it.

Finally she stopped to rest, her furious rush of energy expended. Perspiration trickled down her face, stinging her eyes, and she rubbed it away with the back of a gloved hand, leaving a grimy smear running down her cheek. A cold drink and a shower beckoned enticingly, but she closed her mind to it. First she had to complete her most loathed job of the week.

Gritting her teeth, she moved along the rows of young plants, prising out cartons, half filled with stale beer, that had been sunk into the ground at strategic intervals, and transferred the drowned victims they contained into a bucket. She could cope with spiders, mice, but slugs... With an expression of utter revulsion on her face she began to walk slowly and carefully down to the bottom of the garden.

'Cheerio, Katherine.'

Startled by the drawling voice, Katherine swung round, and the contents of the bucket splashed over her. For a moment she couldn't move, but stood there shuddering convulsively, and then, with an ear-piercing shriek of horror, dropped the bucket and began to run towards the house, colliding straight into Daniel.

'It's only *au revoir*, not farewell,' he murmured soothingly, holding out a steadying hand. 'I'll see you again soon. Try and be brave.'

'Out of my way, you idiot,' Katherine yelped, pushing him aside. Reaching the garden hose, the object of her frantic sprint, she turned it on and doused herself with water, scrubbing her legs and arms ferociously. Sanity slowly returned and with it the awareness that she appeared to have gathered an audience. Daniel and the twins—were they home from school already?—were surveying her with fascinated curiosity.

'Is this a daily ritual?' Daniel enquired gravely.

'Weekly matinées only,' Tim informed him obligingly. 'With the occasional gala evening performance. Advance bookings taken. Reduced rates for parties.'

'We have tried to encourage her to use the shower upstairs, but...' Jessica sighed defeatedly.

'Right. That's it. Floor show's over.' Katherine bowed modestly, switched off the tap and smiled affectionately at her siblings. Twins for sale. Low mileage. All reasonable offers considered. She couldn't bring herself even to look at Daniel. 'I think I'll go and change,' she announced airily, and began to squelch nonchalantly towards the house. She had nearly reached the back door when she slipped in her sodden shoes and glided elegantly on to her bottom. Dignity abandoned, she burst into laughter.

'I should work on the encore. Too predictable,' Daniel advised, looking down at her. 'But then you always have been totally predictable, haven't you, Katherine?' he added softly.

Her grin faded and she scrambled to her feet. Predictable. Sensible. Drenched to the skin. The dust on her arms and legs turned to mud. Hair dripping down her back in rats' tails. So what? A spurt of anger curled deep inside her. She'd never been concerned about Daniel's opinion of her in the past, so why did she care now? Why let him undermine her confidence like this?

Besides, what was wrong with being predictable and sensible?

'Have dinner with me tonight, Katherine.'

'No, thanks.' She pushed open the back door, dismissing the casually tossed invitation out of hand. Daniel had no more desire to spend the evening in her company than she had in his. The insincere invitation was simply an example of his perverse sense of humour.

'I rest my case, m'lord.'

'Very droll.' She flicked him a glance over her shoulder and was momentarily taken aback by the uncharacteristic intentness in his eyes that was at odds with the lazy, drawling voice. She wished she knew what was going on in his head. It had always irked her that, whereas he seemed to be able to guess her thoughts with disconcerting accuracy, she'd never been able to do the same. It had always given him an unfair advantage. 'Aren't you going to be late for your appointment?' she enquired with exaggerated concern.

His scrutiny was beginning to unnerve her and, judging from that sudden gleam in his eyes, he was aware of it and enjoying her increasing discomfort. Quite deliberately his eyes dropped from her face to her damp cotton T-shirt.

'Getting cold?' he asked solicitously.

She flushed scarlet, something she hadn't done since her teens, and bolted into the house, slamming the door shut behind her. She'd always managed to deal with Daniel in the past, had stood her ground, able to either ignore or combat whatever verbal taunt he'd thrown at her. He'd never been able to break her composure or draw her into losing her temper. She bent down and tugged off her shoes. So why did she suddenly feel so vulnerable in his presence? Was it because he knew about

James? Yet he had been remarkably restrained over that particular Achilles' heel, considering the ammunition he now held in his hands. She kicked her shoes across the floor. Even thinking about Daniel made her inexplicably angry.

Damn, she'd forgotten to pay him for the alternator, she suddenly remembered, her memory jogged by the sight of the cheque-book lying on top of the sideboard. Picking up the cheque-book and a pen, she sped through the house to the front door. She had no wish to be in Daniel's debt any longer than necessary, and neither did she want to have to deliberately seek out his company again.

She flung open the front door and saw the Land Rover moving slowly down the drive. The twins were holding the gate open.

'Daniel. Wait a minute,' she yelled, sprinting after it.

He must have seen her in his mirror because the Land Rover came to a halt, and Daniel stuck his head out of the window.

'Changed your mind about tonight? Thought you might,' he drawled as she came up to him. 'I'll pick you up at seven.'

'No, I...' Her words were drowned as he pressed his foot on the accelerator, and with a casual wave of his hand the Land Rover disappeared out of the gate and down the lane.

Katherine turned and stomped towards the house. The insufferable, arrogant... He thought she might change her mind!

'You lucky thing,' Jessica sighed, following her down the hall into the kitchen. 'A date with Daniel,' she murmured dreamily.

'I have not got a date with Daniel,' Katherine muttered. 'I'm not going.'

'Why on earth not?' Her younger sister looked at her incredulously and then smiled encouragingly. 'It would do you good to go out, Kat.'

Amusement at Jessica's motherly tone usurped Katherine's exasperation and she grinned. 'Why? Because I'm getting staid and boring?'

'Well . . .' Jessica flicked a glance at her twin, standing in the doorway. 'I mean, you don't go out that much...and there's a lot more to life than compost heaps and carrots, isn't there?'

'And you needn't worry about the watering or crating up the veg for tomorrow,' Tim chipped in. 'Jess and I can see to that. We haven't got another exam until Friday.' He walked across the floor and picked out an apple from the fruit bowl. 'Wonder if he'll buy it?' he murmured thoughtfully, and ambled from the kitchen.

Katherine looked at Jessica with bewilderment. 'Translation, please. Is who going to buy what?'

'Daniel. Buy Norrington Hall.' Jessica hung up her school blazer behind the kitchen door. 'That's where he's gone now. To meet the estate agent and have a look over the house.' She frowned at her elder sister. 'Didn't Daniel tell you that he was coming back to live in England?'

CHAPTER THREE

CLAD in a white bath-robe, a towel wrapped around her head, Katherine inspected the contents of her wardrobe. Pride demanded that she look her best tonight, and yet some perverse part of her didn't want Daniel to think that she had made a deliberate effort with her appearance in order to impress him. She finally elected for a silky blue cotton summer dress with a discreet neckline and full skirt. Conventional. Safe.

Why was she even going tonight? she wondered, sitting down in front of her dressing-table and blow-drying her hair back away from her face. She still had time to call Daniel and tell him that she'd never had any intention of accepting his invitation and that if he drove over it would be a wasted journey. So why did she keep hesitating to do so?

She was curious, she supposed, and wanted to find out if the twins were correct in their assertion that Daniel was proposing to move back to England. She didn't believe it, was convinced that the twins had misunderstood him. He'd probably been teasing them and they'd taken him at his word. Surely otherwise he would have mentioned his future plans to her? She grimaced. But then when had she and Daniel ever been in the habit of exchanging confidences? They couldn't even hold a normal, rational conversation without sniping at each other. What did he need a house the size of Norrington Hall for, anyway? Perhaps he had illusions of playing lord of the manor, she thought witheringly, and then admitted she was being unfair. Had she had the financial resources she would have been tempted to buy the beautiful old house herself. In many ways she would be glad to see it occupied again; it had saddened her to see it empty for so long. But Daniel . . . virtually a next-door neighbour . . . She refused to even contemplate the idea.

She applied a pink lipstick, blotted it carefully with a tissue, and stared into the mirror. A girl with dark green eyes, flushed cheeks and corn-coloured hair falling over her shoulders gazed back at her uncertainly. Why was she really going out with Daniel tonight? she demanded once again. Because to back out at this late stage would be to admit that she was afraid of something she didn't even understand. Going out to dinner with Daniel tonight was in the nature of a challenge. She had to prove to herself that her immunity to him hadn't weakened, that the spark of physical attraction she'd felt towards him earlier was controllable and had been only a temporary aberration.

Picking up a clutch bag and pushing her feet into a pair of evening sandals, she made her way downstairs to find the twins, and discovered them in the cold larder, storing crates of freshly picked vegetables.

Jessica turned to survey Katherine and her face dropped slightly.

'I thought you were going to wear that sexy green dress you bought for the Sinclairs' New Year's Eve party,' she said with evident disappointment.

The dress to which Jessica referred had been purchased for James's benefit, Katherine remembered with a pang, but, for all the notice he'd paid, she might just as well have worn an old sack. Now even thinking of the dress made her feel foolish.

'You look fine,' Tim assured her. 'Don't forget to take a key in case we're in bed,' he added.

'Do I get a late pass?' Katherine asked drily and wandered restlessly through to the kitchen and out into the back garden. She was ready far too early. What if Daniel didn't even turn up? She ought to be helping the twins...

She heard the sound of footsteps coming up the path and turned round slowly.

'Good evening, Katherine.'

'Hello.' She smiled casually up at Daniel but there was nothing casual about her reaction to the sight of him in a formal, superbly tailored dark suit and brilliant white shirt. Her stomach muscles tightened and her mouth felt dry. It's only Daniel, for heaven's sake, she told herself furiously.

'I'll just fetch my handbag and tell the twins I'm off.' He'd made no comment on her appearance, given her little more than a cursory glance. She wished she'd worn her green dress. No. She wished she were clad in her comfortable, faded jeans and an old T-shirt.

He shortened his stride to match hers as they walked towards the house, and then suddenly paused and surveyed the garden thoughtfully. For a moment she wondered if he was remembering the garden as it used to be, recalling the tennis court, and then she realised that he was studying the row of empty wine bottles planted around the boundary.

'Do they really deter moles?' he asked curiously.

She had anticipated some facetious comment, was taken aback that he had guessed the function of the bottles so accurately.

'They seem to. It's supposed to be the sound of the wind reverberating through the bottles that does the trick.'

'Are moles much of a problem, then?'

'Mmm. There's been a population explosion in many parts of the UK. One theory is that it's due to the decline of the barn owl, one of their predators. Which, of course, is all related to the use of pesticides and throwing nature out of balance.' She sounded like a textbook, and not a particularly original one at that. Why did she feel so jittery and nervous?

'Fascinating,' Daniel murmured, and she stiffened, flicking him a frigid glance. He was laughing at her! Lips compressed together, she increased her pace. Her sense of humour seemed to have evaporated with her self-confidence. The twins teased her unmercifully when she embarked on her favourite hobby-horse, greeting her comments with theatrical yawns, and she never minded.

'Katherine!' Daniel caught hold of her arm and swung her around to face him. 'I'm not mocking you,' he said quietly. 'Most people express concern about the environment, but that's about as far as it goes. You are actually doing something practical about it.'

'In my own small way?' She shook off his hand. 'Don't be so damn patronising.' She could have bitten off her tongue as she saw his face tighten. Why was she deliberately trying to start an argument, not even caring how trivial the cause? 'I'm sorry,' she muttered.

'I'm sick of fighting with you, Katherine,' he said quietly. 'Asking you to dinner was by way of calling a truce but...' He lifted his hands in a gesture of resignation and started to turn away.

Let him go, she ordered herself, gazing after the retreating figure. You didn't want to have dinner with him anyway. You don't care if you never set eyes on Daniel Sinclair again for as long as you live. She tore into the house, grabbed her handbag off the kitchen table and rushed round to the front, coming to an abrupt halt as she saw Daniel leaning indolently against a dark red saloon, the passenger door of which was already open.

He smiled blandly at her rigid figure. 'We'd better make a move if you're ready. I've booked the table for half-past.'

He'd been waiting for her to appear, had expected her to come running, she realised furiously. All that rubbish about a truce, playing the injured, innocent peace-maker... And she'd fallen for it completely, had actually felt ashamed of biting his head off. For two pins she would turn round and march back into the house.

Irresolutely she gazed at him over the roof of the car, and their eyes locked together in a silent battle, a battle that had nothing to do with a dinner invitation but something far more intangible. They were like children in a playground, sizing each other up for a scrap, Katherine thought, and her lips began to twitch.

'How about if we play at adults for the evening?' Daniel queried, grinning back at her.

She ought to be accustomed to his uncanny knack of reading her mind by now, but it still caught her off guard and tonight it made her feel particularly vulnerable. Was she really so painfully transparent? Then, with a jolt, she realised that the answer was far less complex, and wondered why it had never occurred to her before. Daniel wasn't bestowed with some mystical, telepathic power. It was simply that his own thoughts ran on a parallel to her own. It was an oddly disturbing revelation. With an illogical sense of defeat she shrugged, and slid into the passenger seat.

'Shall we have coffee in the lounge?'

Katherine acquiesced with a smile and rose to her feet,

feeling the light touch of Daniel's hand on her elbow as he guided her through the restaurant and into the plush, dimly lit lounge. A small band was playing a medley of slow numbers for the handful of couples on the dance-floor.

As they sat down a pretty dark-haired waitress came towards them, and with wry amusement Katherine noted the expression of undisguised interest on her face as she appraised Daniel.

'Would you like a liqueur?' he asked courteously.

'Just coffee, please.' She'd already drunk more wine than she normally did with the excellent meal, although she'd noted that Daniel, after one pre-dinner whisky, had confined himself to mineral water. Perhaps she would have been wise to have emulated him. She felt strangely light-headed, enveloped in rosy glow of hazy unreality. Not only had she spent the evening with Daniel, but she'd actually enjoyed herself. Except that the man sitting opposite her with the lazy smile on his face wasn't Daniel but a stranger. An attentive, charming, humorous stranger.

Her eyes explored his strong, assured face as if she were seeing it for the first time. There were tiny flecks of dark green in his eyes. She'd never noticed before. She had known this man all her life and yet tonight everything about him seemed alien. He'd been an entertaining companion, his conversation light and amusing—and completely impersonal. She was no nearer knowing his future plans now than she had been at the start of the evening. If he planned to return to live in England he'd given no indication of it, and she'd been reluctant to ask him outright. It suddenly seemed ridiculously important that he tell her of his own accord. She actually minded the fact that he'd told the twins and

not herself, she realised with confusion, smiling automatically as the waitress placed a coffee tray on the table
in front of her. She poured out two cups, handed one
to Daniel, and drank her own swiftly.

'Would you like to dance?' he asked softly and before
she had time to answer he had reached out for her hand
and pulled her to her feet. Wordlessly she allowed him
to lead through the encircling tables and chairs to the
dance-floor, conscious not only of the warm fingers
curved around her palm, but of the number of female
heads that had turned to assess the lean russet-haired
man by her side.

As Daniel's hand dropped to the curve of her waist
and he drew her towards him Katherine was attacked by
self-consciousness. She knew she was unnaturally stiff,
her movements clumsy and awkward. She focused her
eyes at a point above his shoulder to avoid looking directly into his face, but it was impossible not to be aware
of the tenacious jawline and square, decisive chin on a
level with her forehead.

The hand on her back increased its pressure, drawing
her even closer, and she felt the brush of Daniel's jaw
and chin against her hair. She wished she hadn't drunk
her coffee, wished she were still floating in that rosy haze
of well-being, so that her senses were dulled instead of
tuned to this appalling pitch of awareness.

'Recognise this song? It used to be one of your favourites,' Daniel murmured softly, his mouth close to
her ear, his breath warm on her cheek. 'You used to hum
it all the time when you were about seventeen.'

'Did I?' Katherine forced the words out, startled that
he should remember such an insignificant fact about her.
She hadn't even been listening to the music; it had simply
been a background accompaniment to the loud thudding

of her heart. What was happening to her? she wondered uneasily, hating the sensation of being in a situation over which she seemed to have no control at all. Her strongest reaction to Daniel in the past had been indifference. So what had happened to change that, and when had this invidious change occurred?

Concentrate on the music, she ordered herself, and she frowned, beginning to recognise the soft, slow melody. The words of the song formed in her head. When she was seventeen the romantic lyrics had seemed to sum up her newly awakened feelings for James. Now they simply seemed banal and trite.

The song ended, and to her intense relief the band announced that they were taking a short break.

'Ordeal over,' Daniel announced drily, releasing her from the circle of his arms, and she flicked him a quick sideways glance as they began to walk back towards their table. She'd been as animated as a wooden board, she admitted, but to what exactly had he attributed her tenseness? Did he know how unnerved she'd been by his proximity, how some part of her was beginning to recognise and, much against her will, respond to that blatant, potent virility that he exuded like his own personal musk?

'Daniel, old man! Haven't seen you for years!' A stocky fair-haired man blocked their path and pumped Daniel's hand enthusiastically. 'Heard on the grapevine that someone had finally made an honest man of you,' he quipped, smiling warmly at Katherine.

She gave him a lukewarm smile back. This man, whoever he was, had evidently not heard about Daniel's subsequent divorce, and was under the impression that he was still married—and it would appear that she had just been given role of honour as Daniel's wife.

'Hello, Nick,' Daniel greeted him, his face devoid of all expression. 'Nick Harrison, Katherine Maitland,' he continued smoothly, and Katherine saw the faint frown cross over the fair man's face. He'd probably now cast her in role of mistress, she thought with a bubble of amusement, waiting for Daniel to elucidate on the situation and correct whatever misapprehensions Nick Harrison was currently under. She frowned as Daniel made no effort to do so.

'Jan and I are sitting over there. Why don't you come and join us?' Nick Harrison's invitation was a little hesitant, and Katherine was just about to reassure him that he wasn't a party to some illicit affair when she felt a firm hand grip her arm.

'Thanks, Nick. Another time. We were just leaving.'

The hold on Katherine's arm tightened and before she had time to register what was happening, let alone protest, she was skilfully propelled through the tables and chairs to the door. As they emerged into the still night air Katherine shook off Daniel's hand irritably. He hadn't even had the courtesy to ask if she was ready to leave, but had simply marched her out of the lounge like a child. So much for her charming, attentive dinner companion!

'Why didn't you tell your friend you were divorced?' she demanded, eyes dark with exasperation.

'Because I'm not,' he returned curtly and, turning away from her, strode across the car park.

'What? But...' Katherine stared after the retreating figure, trying to combat that sudden inane desire to burst into laughter. Daniel had to be divorced... This was simply another example of his warped sense of humour. He couldn't possibly still be married... could he? She was startled by the fierce wave of resentment that tore through her. He'd no right to have asked her out to dinner tonight, no right to have kissed her yesterday. Admittedly he hadn't lied to her about his marital status because it had never occurred to her to ask, but he must have known that she'd assumed that he was single and he'd made no attempt to disabuse her. Katherine's mouth curved wryly. Wasn't she being rather melodramatic, over-reacting about one fleeting kiss that had been executed merely to taunt her, and a dinner date? And a separated man was hardly in the same category as a married one, was he? A small spurt of anger curdled inside her. But, damn it all, he could have told her!

'Coming?'

Daniel's terse voice cut through her thoughts and, taking a deep breath, she walked swiftly across to the car and slipped in beside him, her expression calm and reposed, determined that he shouldn't suspect just how jolted she'd been by his revelation. He didn't even give her a cursory glance, but merely waited until he heard the click of her seatbelt and then started up the engine.

Turning her head away, Katherine gazed out of the window into the gathering darkness, eyebrows furrowed across her forehead, trying mentally to disassociate herself from the silent man by her side, but seeming to have no control over her errant thoughts. It had been a few months after her parents' death, she recalled, that Daniel had written to his family and informed them of his marriage to a Canadian girl. Still shell-shocked from her recent bereavement, she'd evinced little interest in the news, other than to think privately that it had been somewhat unkind of Daniel to have informed his parents of the *fait accompli* rather than inviting them to the wedding. Perhaps, too, she'd been surprised that he had finally committed himself to one woman. Then, that

Christmas, Daniel had returned to England alone and she'd learned via James that his wife had simply walked out of their matrimonial home one morning and never returned. Katherine, her sympathies entirely with the girl, who must have been so desperately unhappy to have taken such drastic measures, had assumed that a divorce was impending.

Katherine's frown deepened. Why hadn't Daniel implemented divorce proceedings against his wife? She had no idea of the divorce laws in Canada, but surely desertion was ample grounds? It probably suited him to have a theoretical wife, she thought contemptuously. He could live the life of a bachelor and yet have an escape clause should any woman demand a permanent commitment from him.

Unable to resist the temptation any longer, she flicked Daniel a sideways glance, her eyes moving over the tenacious square jaw, absorbing the grim lines etched around his straight mouth. She had misjudged him completely, she admitted with a curious flip of her stomach. His reaction tonight to Nick Harrison's unintentional gaffe indicated that he hadn't completely come to terms with his failed marriage, nor dismissed it as lightly as she'd originally supposed. He was angry, she could sense it, but was that anger directed against himself or the woman who'd had the temerity to walk out on him? Was it simply that his male ego had been badly dented, or were the wounds deeper than that? Perhaps he was still in love with his wife, still hoping for a reconciliation. She didn't even know his wife's name, Katherine realised, and yet she seemed to have a clear mental picture of her in her mind: small, dark-haired, sophisticated. Yet apparently still naïve and gullible enough to have been conned by Daniel's lazy charm—she'd nearly fallen for it herself tonight, she admitted, but that temporary danger was well past.

She dropped her eyes from Daniel's face, conscious that she'd been watching him longer than she'd intended. It was odd, she reflected, to think that Daniel might be suffering just as she was suffering over James. It should have brought them closer, created some sort of tenuous bond between them, and yet conversely the barrier that had existed between them for years seemed even more insurmountable. His marriage, like the injury to his leg, was another taboo subject she would never dare broach with him.

Restlessly she moved in her seat. Daniel seemed to have forgotten her existence completely, locked in his own private world, his eyes never once straying from the road ahead. He could make some effort at conversation, Katherine thought irritably, though, to be fair, she supposed, there was nothing to stop her taking the initiative and breaking the silence. And say what exactly? She racked her brain for some startling, world-shattering remark that couldn't fail to evoke a response from Daniel, but her inventiveness seemed to have deserted her. Admitting defeat, she stared resignedly out of the window at the passing, shadowy countryside.

The gates at the bottom of the drive had been left open, and the moment the car drew to a halt in front of the house Katherine reached for the door-handle.

'Goodnight,' she muttered abruptly as she scrambled out. It seemed utterly farcical after the strained, uncomfortable journey home to thank Daniel blithely for a pleasant evening. Without a backward glance she began to walk swiftly towards the front door, and paused reluctantly as she heard footsteps behind her.

'Katherine. I didn't intend the evening to end like this.'

Slowly and unwillingly she turned round and faced Daniel. In retrospect, she wasn't at all sorry that the evening had ended as it had. That short, sharp shock imparted by Nick Harrison had been exactly what she'd needed to bring her back to her senses. Nothing had changed between herself and Daniel, and nothing ever would.

'And how exactly did you intend the evening to end?' she enquired caustically and then cringed, wishing she'd thought before speaking. It sounded as if she were being provocative, virtually inviting him to kiss her... Quickly she mounted the two wide steps to the front door and fished in her handbag for her key.

'I had visions of us drinking coffee in your kitchen, swapping gardening tips,' Daniel murmured solemnly by her side, and she faltered, thrown off balance by his sudden change of mood. Light issuing from the hall window illuminated the planes of his face. The lines of tension had eased and his eyes glinted with the familiar mockery as he looked down at her. Instantly distrustful, Katherine took a wary step backwards, but she was too late as his hands snaked out, caught hold of her shoulders and drew her towards him.

'Goodnight, Katherine,' he murmured, lowering his head slowly and purposefully.

She didn't want to play this ridiculous game any longer, Katherine told herself firmly. Push him away, turn your head to one side. If only she could break his gaze, glance away, but she seemed mesmerised, her eyes locked into the golden tawny ones. She could feel the warmth of his breath on her face, the firm, straight mouth now barely an inch from her own. She couldn't think coherently any longer, confused by that pounding in her head. Her eyelashes flickered downwards, her lips parted and tilted upwards to meet his.

She felt Daniel's mouth brush her forehead in the briefest of chaste salutations, realised that his hands had dropped from her shoulders, and her eyes jerked open. She couldn't bear to look at Daniel, couldn't bear to witness the expression of satisfaction and amusement etched on his face, hated him so much in that moment that it was a physical pain inside her. What a fool she must have looked, standing there submissively in front of him, eyes closed ... Clumsily she turned away from him, mechanically looking in her bag for the front-door key before realising it was clutched tightly in her left hand. Why had he deliberately humiliated her like this, or had she wrought the humiliation on herself, completely misread the situation? Blood scalded her cheeks. For one mad second she'd actually wanted Daniel to kiss her, to feel his arms around her, and, worst of all, he was now fully aware of that fact.

Unsteadily she inserted the key in the lock and nearly fell headlong into the hall as the door was opened from the other side.

'Oh, it's you. Had a good evening?' Tim stood there, clad in pyjamas and dressing-gown. 'I heard the car and thought it was Jesse. She forgot to take a key,' he added casually.

Thank heavens Jesse was out, Katherine thought instantly. The last thing she could have dealt with at the moment was an enthusiastic barrage of questions about Daniel from her younger sister. Then her eyebrows drew together, the full implication of Tim's words finally dawning on her. 'You mean Jesse has gone out? Where to?' No wonder Jessica had been so keen to encourage her to go out tonight.

'Andy Coles turned up after you'd left and Jesse went back to his house to watch a video,' Tim explained casually, and grinned over her shoulder. 'Hello, Daniel.'

'Who on earth's Andy Coles?' Katherine demanded. Even before Tim's greeting she had sensed the male presence behind her. Perhaps her memory was failing but she couldn't recall inviting Daniel in, she thought sourly. It was tempting to turn round and haughtily order him out of her home but that would involve complicated explanations to a doubtlessly startled Tim.

'You saw him the other day. In the market place.'

'The boy on the motorbike . . .' She saw Tim's nod of affirmation and froze inside. 'You let Jesse go off on the back of his bike . . . why didn't you stop her, Tim? You know how dangerous they are . . .' It had been in order to avoid hitting a motor-cyclist who hadn't stopped at a junction that her father's car had swerved off the road and into a tree. If anything happened to Jesse . . . Tim was staring at her and she saw the rare glint of anger in his eyes.

'Andy's borrowed his father's car for the evening,' he said shortly. 'Do you think . . . ?'

Instantly Katherine was swamped by guilt. She should have known Tim would have stopped his twin, by force if necessary, from riding pillion on a motorbike. 'I'm sorry,' she said quietly, trying to keep both her voice and expression calm. 'Where does Andy live?'

'In that house with the white fence at the end of James's street. His family moved in there about a month ago.'

'Right.' She marched to the end of the hall and picked up the telephone. 'I'll call James and ask him to go down and fetch Jesse. He can take her back to the cottage and I'll go over and pick her up.' She glanced at Tim over her shoulder. 'Would you go and fetch the van keys, please? They should be on the hook in the kitchen.'

He looked back at her uncomprehendingly. 'There's no need to worry, Kat. Andy's a nice bloke. He was in the year above us at school until he left to go to college, and his sister's in the same class as Jesse. Just 'cause he rides a motorbike sometimes doesn't mean——'

'Just get the keys,' Katherine said shortly. She'd just started to dial the familiar number when the telephone was wrestled unceremoniously out of her hand.

'What exactly are you playing at?' Daniel enquired conversationally, replacing the receiver. 'Jessica has gone over to a friend's house for the evening. Why the big drama?'

'You've really no idea at all, have you?' Katherine glared at him, the calm reasonableness in his voice almost more than she could stand. 'I'm responsible for Jesse. I don't know the first thing about this boy she's out with tonight.' Why didn't she simply tell Daniel to go home and stop interfering in something that was nothing to do with him?

'Don't you trust Jesse, credit her with any sense? She'll be seventeen in a few months, for Pete's sake.'

'So I should just go calmly to bed? Ignore the fact that my younger sister is out at this time of night...?'

'Ten o'clock?' He quirked an eyebrow at her.

Is that all it was? Katherine glanced at her wrist-watch for confirmation. She'd completely lost track of time, had thought it was midnight at least... but then her evening had been curtailed, she remembered. She hesitated, hand hovering near the phone.

'You can't go on running to James every time you get hysterical over some minor domestic problem.' Daniel's eyes narrowed contemptuously. 'Or is this just another

excuse to see him?' He paused and added with great deliberation, 'Robyn was around there when I left this
evening. I doubt if James is going to be overjoyed if you
disturb him just to go on some ridiculous errand.'

She stiffened. What was he trying to imply? That
James and Robyn might be at this very moment in bed
together? Tight-lipped, she dragged a jacket from one
of the hooks on the wall and, armed with the keys Tim
had thrust into her hand, marched out of the door.

'We'll use my car. You've had too much to drink.'
Daniel towered in front of her, blocking her way to the
van.

She looked up at him incredulously. Was there no end
to this man's arrogance? He'd walked into her home uninvited, prevented her from using her own telephone,
and was now ordering her not to drive her own van. But
she didn't have time to argue now, and anyway common
sense told her that Daniel was right. Although she felt
stone-cold sober, she had drunk more that evening than
she normally did, she admitted.

Acquiescing with a grudging nod, she followed him
to his car. She supposed she ought to feel grateful to
Daniel for offering to drive her over to the Coleses'
house, but it was a sentiment she found difficult to extend
towards him, resenting being in his debt in any form at
all. Why was he involving himself in her problem
anyway?

Silently she slid into the passenger-seat beside him,
staring rigidly ahead as the car moved smoothly down
the drive. A knot was forming in the pit of her stomach,
the fear she'd thought she'd finally managed to come to
terms with crawling over her with all its old remembered
intensity. Jessica might at this very moment be on her
way home. They might be too late.

'And what do you propose to do exactly when we arrive at the Coleses'? Storm the house and drag Jessica out kicking and screaming?'

Katherine's eyes flickered briefly to Daniel's face, letting the flippant words wash over her. He thought she was over-reacting, behaving like a neurotic, hysterical female, and yet she didn't seem to have the energy to retaliate or defend herself. The initial wave of panic had ebbed, leaving her drained, empty and quite appallingly lonely. Her gaze dropped to the lean, strong fingers resting lightly around the steering-wheel, guiding the powerful car along the narrow, winding lanes towards the small market town. How was it possible to be sitting so close to another human being and feel so isolated and alone? She desperately wanted to unburden herself of those nightmarish anxieties she'd kept bottled up for so long, but Daniel was the last person in the world in whom she'd ever confide or from whom she'd seek re-assurance. Even if she managed to express those fears out loud, he didn't possess the sensitivity to understand them. Why couldn't it have been sympathetic, de-pendable James sitting beside her now instead of Daniel? She was shocked by the ferocity of the resentment swelling up inside her and even more confused by the knowledge that the anger was directed solely at Daniel, and not, as would surely have been more logical, against the man who had caused her, albeit unintentionally, so much anguish.

The car moved along the deserted high street and turned left into the familiar narrow street. She sensed Daniel's fleeting, exploratory glance as they passed James's cottage and, summoning every ounce of will-power, kept her eyes fixed steadily ahead, her expression deadpan. What had Daniel been hoping she'd do anyway, she wondered caustically—heave a deep sigh of anguish, gaze up at James's window with hopeless, adoring eyes like some lovelorn teenager?

'Here we are,' Daniel announced with a cheerfulness that set her teeth on edge as he drew to a halt at the end of the street. 'So what's the plan? Do we maintain a discreet observation for a while, or go into battle immediately?'

'You can do what the hell you like,' Katherine snapped, jumping out of the car and slamming the door soundly behind her. He could ridicule her all he liked. She didn't care. He had absolutely no comprehension of what she was going through, was treating this whole episode like some huge joke.

She opened a white wooden gate and started to march purposefully up the path towards the solid red-bricked house in front of her. As she approached the front door her confidence, without warning, deserted her, doubts assailing her for the first time. She shouldn't have given way to that initial burst of panic, shouldn't have come tearing over here until she'd had a chance to calm down and think more rationally. Jessica was going to be furious, she thought unhappily, her hand hovering near the doorbell. It wasn't too late to beat a hasty retreat, even now. She flicked an indecisive glance back over her shoulder and towards the car and saw Daniel lift his hand in a casual wave, and made up her mind. Determinedly she pressed the doorbell. She simply couldn't scurry back to the car, admit she'd acted foolishly and meekly ask Daniel to drive her home.

The door opened and a plump, pleasant-faced woman who looked vaguely familiar smiled at her enquiringly.

'Mrs Cole? I'm Katherine Maitland…Jessica's sister.'

'Oh, yes, of course. I've seen you in the market. Do come in. The film's just finished and I was just about to make some coffee. Would you like some?'

'No, thank you.' Katherine refused the offer with a smile, disconcerted and yet relieved that the older woman seemed to accept her unexpected and unexplained presence quite matter-of-factly and ruefully hoping that Jessica would be as accommodating.

'I've never been so humiliated in all my life. As soon as I leave school next month I'm going to get a job and move into a flat of my own.' Jessica stamped up and down the kitchen floor. 'Coming to collect me as if I were a five-year-old!'

Resisting the temptation to inform her sister that at present she was behaving like a five-year-old, Katherine set a saucepan of milk on the stove. 'Cocoa?'

'It would choke me!'

Jessica flounced out of the room and slammed the door ferociously behind her.

'Think I'll go to bed, too.' With an expression of acute discomfort on his face, Tim pushed back his chair and rose to his feet. 'See you in the morning, Kat. Goodnight, Daniel.' He paused in the doorway, as if about to say something else, evidently changed his mind and vanished into the hall.

Poor Tim, torn between loyalty to his twin and embarrassment that her tantrum had been witnessed by an outsider, Katherine thought with a suppressed sigh, mechanically stirring cocoa powder into a smooth paste. After Daniel had driven herself and a silent, sulky Jessica home from the Coleses', she'd had no real option other than to invite him into the house, but she hadn't actually

thought he would accept the invitation, had taken it for
granted that he would have the tact to refuse.

After discarding his jacket and loosening his tie he
had commandeered her own favourite seat, an old
wooden rocking-chair, and was sitting with his long legs
stretched out indolently in front of him, arms folded
behind his head, looking totally unperturbed by Jessica's
outburst.

The milk came to the boil and Katherine poured it
into two mugs, stirring the contents vigorously.

'Haven't had cocoa for years,' Daniel commented idly
as she handed him a mug.

She shrugged and remained standing, leaning back
against the sink unit, her fingers curled around her own
mug. Perhaps she should have offered him a choice of
beverage; perhaps he didn't even like cocoa . . . Why, she
wondered fleetingly, did she always assume that Daniel
was being derogatory? His remark about the cocoa had
been perfectly innocuous and yet she was automatically
looking for some implied criticism.

'What's Jessica planning to do when she leaves
school?' Casually Daniel crossed one leg over a knee,
the dark trousers tautening along the line of his muscular thighs.

Katherine focused her eyes at a point above the russet
head. Couldn't he appreciate that the last thing she felt
like discussing now was Jessica? She felt emotionally and
physically drained, just wanted to Daniel to leave so that
she could go to bed, sink into oblivion and forget the
whole dreadful day. 'Jesse helps out at the local riding
stables at weekends and she's hoping she'll be offered a
permanent part-time job,' she finally answered
reluctantly.

'And you are naturally opposed to the idea and are going to insist she studies for her A levels.'

Katherine ignored the challenge in the drawling voice. She swallowed her cocoa, turned towards the sink and rinsed her mug in hot running water. She refused to be drawn into a discussion about Jessica's future. It was nothing to do with Daniel. With great deliberation she studied the clock on the wall. 'I have to be up at five.'

To her intense relief Daniel stretched his arms above his head and rose obligingly to his feet. 'Thanks. It was delicious.' He handed her his empty mug, started towards the door and swung round. 'So, what was tonight really all about, Katherine?' he demanded quietly. 'You didn't get in a blind panic simply because Jessica went over to Andy Coles's house to watch a film, did you?'

Katherine stiffened, and picked up a tea-towel. 'I don't know what you're talking about.' Furiously she began to dry Daniel's unwashed mug.

'Don't you?' He quirked a sceptical dark eyebrow. 'When I drove back from the Coleses' tonight you were terrified. You were gripping the edge of the seat, your eyes kept darting to the speedometer, your foot slammed down on an imaginary brake every time you saw an on-coming car.'

Katherine flushed but returned his gaze steadily. 'Perhaps I don't have any confidence in your driving ability,' she said evenly. She looked down with surprise at the mug in her hands and placed it in the sink.

'Sorry, but that won't do.' Daniel shook his head dismissively. 'You were perfectly happy to let me drive you yesterday and earlier this evening. But of course Jessica wasn't in the car then.'

Katherine gazed at him warily, suspicious and confused by the unexpected gentleness both in his voice and eyes.

'This has something to do with your parents' accident, doesn't it?'

She whirled away and slumped down in the nearest chair. Propping her elbows on the table in front of her, she cupped her chin in her hands and gazed unseeingly at the wall.

'It might help to talk about it.' Daniel pulled up a chair beside her.

'Pretend you're that stranger on a train?' Her flippancy was contrived, a deliberate shield for that pain and anger starting to invade her. 'Or my personal therapist?'

'You could try pretending I was a friend.'

'I'm the practical type.' She shot him a sideways glance, uncertain of how to interpret that last remark, but learned nothing from the strong, impassive profile. 'I don't possess that degree of imagination.' Her eyes dropped to his hands, resting lightly on the table, palms downwards, long, lean fingers with the surgically clean nails splayed out. What would it be like to stop fighting with Daniel and have him as a friend? To feel comfortable, unconstrained, at peace in his company? It was a pointless speculation. Daniel wasn't the type of man to form a platonic friendship with a woman, and anything else was inconceivable.

The ticking of the wall clock seemed deafening in the still kitchen. She sensed the tawny-golden gaze on her face, knew that Daniel was waiting for her to speak and recoiled mentally from the feeling of being pressurised. She wasn't going to bare her soul to Daniel, didn't want to talk about the past, didn't want to remember that night.

'I'm going to bed,' she muttered gruffly, scraping back her chair and rising jerkily to her feet. He could see himself out, do what he liked; she didn't care.

'Do you still hold me responsible for your parents' death?'

CHAPTER FOUR

KATHERINE gripped the back of the chair and stared at Daniel uncomprehendingly as his words slowly filtered into her brain. 'I don't understand ... it was the motorcyclist ...' She faltered, shocked by the raw, naked emotion on his face, the tearing pain in his eyes.

'It was I who gave your parents the theatre tickets that night. They were complimentary ones and I'd already seen the play in London.' His voice thickened. 'If only I hadn't given ...'

If only he hadn't given her parents the tickets they wouldn't have been driving back from the theatre late that night, wouldn't have encountered that drunken motor-cyclist, Katherine completed the words in her head. Dazedly she walked over to the window and stared out into the darkness. All these years Daniel had held himself responsible for initiating the sequence of events that had culminated in her parents' death.

'I didn't know. About the tickets,' she muttered. And, now she did know, how did she feel? Perhaps four years ago when she'd been so bitter, angry with the whole world, some of those destructive emotions might have irrationally and unfairly been directed at Daniel. But not now. She turned round to face him and her throat constricted. There was a tightness in her chest that had nothing to do with the past tragedy. She couldn't bear to see that look of tortuous self-recrimination in his eyes, desperately wanted it to be replaced by the familiar, mocking glint, ached to see the corners of the straight mouth quirk into that slow, lazy smile.

'You weren't responsible in any way for what happened to my parents.' Her eyes locked into his and she knew in that moment that he would understand about her own personal nightmare, knew too that she wanted to tell him. Only half aware of what she was doing, she began to pace up and down the kitchen, her eyes focused on the floor. 'The night of the accident...' her voice was low but steady '...I had just come home from college for the summer vacation and was minding the twins.' Of course, he would know that anyway. 'I didn't wait up for Mum and Dad, just went to bed.' Her voice wavered, but she forced herself to go on. 'I don't know what time it was, but I was woken by the doorbell. I thought they'd forgotten their key... but it was a policewoman.' She came to a halt and looked at Daniel. 'A few months later the twins went to watch the school play. I had a stinking cold and couldn't go with them, so one of their friend's parents took them. They were nearly an hour late arriving home. Apparently the car had broken down. But all the time...'

'You were waiting for that policewoman to appear,' Daniel completed quietly.

She nodded. 'For a long time after that I couldn't bear the twins to be driven by anyone else but me or...'

'James?' He lifted a dark eyebrow.

'Yes.' She tried to smile, but the attempt was unsuccessful. 'I thought I'd finally managed to come to terms with it all. And then tonight, thinking of Jesse being driven home in the dark by a young, inexperienced driver...' She lifted her hands in a gesture of defeat.

'I'm neither young nor inexperienced.' Daniel rose to his feet and moved towards her. 'So why were you so

damn frightened when I drove you home with Jessica?'
He looked down at her, arms folded across his chest.
All signs of gentleness were erased from his face. His
eyes were cool, his mouth straight and unsmiling.

'I kept thinking, if anything happened to Jesse and
me, Tim would be left on his own.' He was going to
think her completely neurotic, she thought with
mounting embarrassment, beginning to wonder what had
ever possessed her to confide in him. She was bewildered by his abrupt transformation. For a few moments
she'd actually felt close to Daniel, had felt as if she were
finally beginning to penetrate that barrier that separated
them, and yet now he seemed as remote and as unap-
proachable as ever. She felt curiously bereft. She'd liked
that man with the warm, compassionate eyes and strong,
gentle face. She'd liked a man who didn't exist, she admitted wryly. Daniel wasn't concerned about her, merely
irritated because she had apparently cast aspersions about
his driving prowess.

'Do the twins know how you feel?'

'No.' She wanted to let the subject drop. She felt
foolish and self-conscious. 'Tim doesn't say much, seems
quite happy to let me ferry him everywhere. But Jesse
just thinks I'm the bossy, big sister. That I'm over-
protective.' Oh, God, she was going to cry. She'd
managed to talk about her parents relatively calmly, so
why on earth did she have to start blubbering now? She
spun away from Daniel, surreptitiously dashing the back
of her hand across her face, but the salty tears continued
to stream down her cheeks.

'Something in my eye,' she mumbled incoherently, and
the next moment she found herself encircled by a pair
of strong arms, her head being pushed into the crook
of a hard shoulder.

The flow of tears halted and dried on her cheek. Adrenalin spurted through her veins, her senses rebelling against the sudden, unexpected physical contact. The upper half of her body was pressed against a wall of solid muscle; her whole being was infiltrated by unwanted malenesss.

'It's all right, Katherine,' a deep voice murmured softly. 'Just cry if you want to.'

'Sob my heart out against your manly chest?' she growled under her breath, glowering at the chin on a level with her forehead. It was far from all right! There was nothing remotely soothing or comforting about being held in Daniel's arms. She would just as soon nestle up to a man-eating tiger. A deft hand was stroking her hair, making her scalp tingle, sending shock waves down her spine.

'Did you know you have the most beautiful neck?' Daniel murmured huskily above her head, pushing back the soft corn-coloured hair behind her ears and brushing the sensitive skin he'd exposed with his lips.

She blotted out his words, refused to acknowledge those sensations sweeping through her, tormenting her nerve-endings. She started to ease herself away from him, but the arm around her shoulder tightened.

'Daniel.' Determinedly she addressed the collar of his shirt. She couldn't bring herself to look at him directly. 'I'm fine now. You can—er—let me go.'

With relief she felt his arms relax their hold, but then realised he was merely changing his stance. One hand dropped to her waist, drawing her towards him, moulding her hips into his hard thighs. He lifted his other hand to her face and his lean fingers slowly traced a lingering path over the contours of her cheeks and moved to outline the curve of her lips.

'Daniel . . .'

'What's the matter, Katherine? What are you frightened of?'

The mocking challenge in his voice served to reinforce her defences. She tilted her head and considered him with cool, unwavering eyes.

'Oh, all the usual things,' she murmured glibly. 'Thunderstorms, dark alleys, things that go bump in the night.' She knew she hadn't fooled him for a second and her eyes dilated with panic as he bent to kiss her throat. His lips trailed a slow, sensuous path to her ear, teasing the delicate whorls with an expert tongue.

Why was he doing this to her? Katherine thought desperately, trying to fight the warm rush of tantalising pleasure swirling through her. What was he trying to prove? Just how damn irresistible he was? Why didn't she protest, push him away with all her force? She didn't seem to have the energy to do anything. She couldn't seem to think straight any more, felt dizzy, light-headed, as if she'd just swallowed a bottle of champagne. She could feel her heart thudding against her rib-cage, could hardly breathe . . .

Her arms of their own volition stretched up and curled around Daniel's neck, a feeling of overwhelming relief shuddering through her as his mouth finally took possession of hers. His kiss deepened, his tongue probing the inner moistness between her parted, pliant lips as his hands swept caressingly down the length of her body.

Eyes closed, Katherine felt herself spinning out of control, lost in a whirlpool of pleasure. There was nothing in the world but this man with the increasingly urgent mouth and hands. She heard the rasp of a zip and shivered with shocked delight as his hand seared her naked flesh, his fingers beginning to move in languorous circles across her rib-cage and upwards to cup the rounded swell of her breasts. His fingers slipped beneath the lace bra, his thumbs beginning to brush across the taut, hardening nipples in a teasing, sensual rhythm.

Instinctively, responding to that aching need inside her, Katherine arched her hips against him, her hands tightening on his shoulders, drowning in the waves of exquisite pleasure sweeping over her. Dazedly her eyes flickered open, and she looked up at him, wanting to see the expression on his face, wanting to know if touching her gave him the same degree of intense pleasure, wanting to discover if her body pleased him. His blurred features swam before her and then slowly her eyes began to focus more clearly, and she saw the glint of satisfaction in his eyes, the smile quirking the corners of his mouth as he gazed down into her flushed face.

The warmth seeped from her body, her thick lashes dropping down protectively over her eyes so that he wouldn't see the shocked hurt in them. He was laughing at her! This was all just a game to him. He was playing with her, just as he'd played with her earlier that evening outside the front door. Did it give his male ego a fillip to see just how easily he could arouse her, mould her into a submissive, suppliant, mindless lump of putty under his expert, coaxing hands? Her stomach curdled, nausea engulfing her. Somehow she had to salvage some remnants of pride.

Eyes tightly closed, she swayed against him. Even now, she thought with self-loathing, her traitorous body was still alive to those skilled, seductive hands, making it hard for her to remain clear-headed. She laced her fingers around the back of his head and stretched up, covering his face with small, feverish, open-mouthed kisses, moving down his jaw, to his throat.

'Oh, James,' she murmured huskily, 'James...'

His reaction was as immediate as she'd hoped. His body stiffened against her and he drew away, his arms dropping to his side.

'It was a slip... I'm sorry,' she mumbled, her voice high and flustered as she acted out her role. She braced herself for his anger and contempt, knowing that it would merely be a shield for his injured masculine pride at the discovery that she had been using him as a substitute, responding to another man in her imagination. Disconcerted by his continuing silence, she looked up at him warily. His face was devoid of all emotion, completely impassive, his eyes dark and unreadable.

'Goodnight, Katherine.' Casually he picked up his jacket, slung it over his shoulder and crossed the kitchen with long, easy strides.

'Daniel...' He didn't even give her a backward glance, but simply closed the door quietly behind him.

Katherine swallowed, rooted to the spot. There was no feeling of victory, just emptiness. Nothing had turned out as she'd anticipated. She hadn't even dented his ego, merely made a first-class idiot of herself. What if she'd misjudged Daniel completely, had misinterpreted that expression on his face, had reacted with her habitual over-sensitivity where he was concerned? It had been such a cheap, petty thing to do, she thought with self-revulsion, wishing with all her heart she could put the clock back just a few short minutes. No, longer than that. She should never have let the situation develop as it had in the first place. It was just that she'd been upset, vulnerable... and Daniel had taken advantage of her weakened state...

'For Pete's sake,' she exploded out loud, her eyes dark with disgust. 'Be honest at least with yourself.' Daniel hadn't forced himself on her; she could have extricated herself from his arms at any time if she'd really tried. But she hadn't wanted to. Hell, she thought vehemently, she wished she had been fantasising about James, had genuinely been using Daniel as a substitute for his brother in her imagination. At least that would have explained her response to a man she neither liked nor respected.

Automatically she locked the back door, switched off all the downstairs lights and made her way up the stairs to her bedroom. There was no point in continuing with this post-mortem. She couldn't change what had happened, so she had to simply put it out of her mind. And there was one consolation—Daniel would certainly never deliberately seek out her company or attempt to touch her again. And that would suit her just fine!

The triumphal wedding march echoed around the packed church as the bridal party emerged from the vestry and began its slow procession down the aisle.

'Doesn't she look beautiful?' murmured a misty-eyed woman sitting in the same pew as Katherine.

Pretty would be a more accurate description of the approaching bride, Katherine decided thoughtfully. Pretty in a rather obvious way. She could appreciate that Robyn had probably been nervous while preparing for her big day, but it was regrettable that the New Zealand girl had been quite so heavy-handed with her make-up. And those voluptuous curves would doubtlessly give way to plumpness, possibly obesity with the passage of time. Cat, Katherine's better self reproved her. Well, didn't she have some justification for being catty about the girl who had stolen James away from her? Except that James had never been hers in the first place, she reminded herself. She braced herself for that stab of agonising pain, but nothing happened.

It was completely mystifying. She had dreaded this day for so long and yet, now it had finally arrived, she felt absolutely no emotion at all. She'd viewed the whole ceremony with complete clinical detachment. The twins, on either side of her, hadn't nudged her at any point, so presumably she'd stood, knelt and opened her hymn book as required, although she had no clear recollection of doing any of those things. Even the sound of James's firm, clear voice affirming his wedding vows had left her unmoved. Thoughtfully she studied her hands, fascinated by the delicate pink nail polish that was the exact match for her pink silk dress and jacket.

'Kat, come on.'

Roused by Jessica's voice, Katherine glanced up and with complete bewilderment realised that the congregation was filing out of the church. She seemed to have completely blanked out the last few seconds, couldn't remember James actually passing her pew. She rose to her feet and walked down the aisle towards the door.

'You forgot your handbag!' Jessica thrust it into her hand as they emerged into the late-afternoon sunshine and joined the other guests milling around on the lawn in front of the church.

'Oh, lord, I suppose we've got to hang about for the photographs now,' Tim muttered under his breath and disappeared into the crowd, followed by his twin.

Absently Katherine smiled at the many familiar faces surging around her. She'd met most of James's numerous relatives over the years, had always thought that one day she would become a member of that large family. Her eyes rested on Robyn as she stood on the church steps, hand resting possessively on her husband's arm, smiling radiantly at the photographer. Then, for the first time that day, Katherine looked directly at James, registering the expression of love and pride on his face as he gazed down at his bride. The new Mrs James Sinclair.

Katherine felt as if she were emerging from a long, foggy tunnel, waking up from a deep trance... This was reality. James and Robyn. Man and wife. She swallowed hard, trying to dislodge that lump in her throat, staring down at the grass. If only she could just escape somewhere on her own for a few moments.

'I don't think I've ever seen James look so happy,' a familiar voice drawled behind her.

You absolute bastard, Katherine thought silently, having no doubt at whom the seemingly innocuous remark was directed. She had accepted that it would be impossible to avoid Daniel completely today, but had assumed that he would want to give her as wide a berth as she did him. But evidently the temptation to taunt her, to turn the knife deeper in the wound, had proved to be too irresistible. How unerringly he had chosen the moment when she was at her most vulnerable.

'Hello, Daniel,' she greeted him equably, determined not to show any extreme of emotion, and smiled casually at the woman hanging on to his arm. Dark hair. Large brown eyes. Petite. Daniel was running true to form, she thought acidly. Could he actually differentiate between all the countless look-alike brunettes she'd seen in his company over the years, or did they simply merge into one nameless face and body in his mind? How appallingly shallow he was, not to mention chauvinistic, to be attracted to a woman solely because she measured up to a very exact physical ideal.

'Julia Peterson, Katherine Maitland,' Daniel smiled blandly. 'Katherine's an old friend of James's.'

'We were at school together.' Katherine smiled back with equal blandness. If anyone had shown her the least bit of sympathy a few moments ago she would have probably disgraced herself and burst into tears. But Daniel's barbs had the reverse effect, strengthened her resolve to get through the day with complete equanimity. There was nothing he could do or say to break her composure, she thought with satisfaction, meeting the golden gaze serenely. He'd had his hair cut, she observed, but the hairdresser hadn't managed to completely tame that lion's mane, and an unruly lock sprang across his forehead. She dropped her eyes quickly, shocked to discover how much she longed to reach up a hand and brush that wilful lock back from his face.

'Bridegroom and bridesmaids, please.' The photographer gestured in their direction.

'That's your cue, darling.' The dark-haired woman turned to Daniel, picked off an imaginary speck from his dark suit and readjusted his buttonhole with a proprietorial air that was indicative of more than just a casual acquaintance and which Katherine found profoundly irritating. She watched Daniel move with long, loping strides across the grass, her irritation intensifying as she observed the number of female eyes that were also following his progress. James and Robyn were supposed to be the star turn today, not Daniel! Yet already the latter seemed to be commanding most of the attention.

The sun glinted on his hair, firing it with red flames as he smiled lazily towards the photographer, and Katherine's stomach dipped, the sheer force of Daniel's attraction jolting her like an electric shock wave. For years she'd witnessed Daniel's effect on women, had watched them vying for his attention, wondering with a mixture of scorn and derision if she was the only sane member of her sex left on the planet. She'd been so complacent, so certain of her own in-built immunity to Daniel, and now that immunity seemed to be crumbling, brick by brick. Each time she saw him, she admitted uneasily, it was becoming more and more difficult to avoid being drawn into that golden snare that he cast around him with such effortless ease. Damn it, she thought savagely, she was not going to let her treacherous hormones override her common sense and alter her opinion of Daniel.

'You'd think he'd be such an arrogant devil, but he's the most unassuming man I've ever met.'

Katherine's eyes shot to the dark-haired woman by her side, wondering if she'd missed something. Surely Julia Peterson wasn't talking about Daniel...? She began to choke and hurriedly fished in her handbag for a handkerchief. 'Tickle in my throat,' she muttered, managing a realistic cough. Daniel, unassuming? Any moment now, Julia would be informing her that he was shy and retiring!

Her gaze flickered appraisingly over the other woman, aware that she had been subject to a similar discreet scrutiny. Those long, sweeping dark lashes couldn't possibly be natural, nor those long, beautifully manicured red nails. What on earth was the matter with her today? Katherine pulled herself up short. She was really living up to the feline derivative of her name—would be developing a fur coat and whiskers if she wasn't careful! Her aversion to Robyn, although hardly commendable, was understandable, but to feel such an immediate antipathy towards someone with whom she'd yet to ex-

change a single word was totally uncharacteristic and
inexplicable.

'Have you known Daniel long?' she asked casually.
The question had been prompted purely out of politeness, a means of making amends for her uncharitable
thoughts, and not, of course, because she was the least
bit curious about Julia's relationship with Daniel.

'We were at university together, and meet up whenever
Daniel's in London. We were very close for a while but
then Daniel began to work abroad such a lot.' Julia
shrugged elegant shoulders, and then smiled. 'Of course,
now he's decided to settle in England and is buying that
gorgeous old house ... who knows what may happen?'

Katherine smiled back. Unfair though it might be to
form an opinion of someone on so short an acquaintance, the fact remained that her initial antipathy
to Julia Peterson seemed to be increasing by the second.
'You've actually seen Norrington Hall?' She was startled
by the slight catch in her voice.

'Mmm. Daniel showed me around yesterday
afternoon.'

So Julia hadn't arrived from London this morning,
as she'd originally supposed, but had spent yesterday
with Daniel as well. And last night? The fact that Daniel
was still married was evidently of no consequence to
Julia. Presumably her views on fidelity were the same
as his, Katherine thought caustically. Was Julia one of
the reasons Daniel had decided to return to England per-
manently? He certainly hadn't lost much time in resuming their relationship.

She didn't want to stand here talking to Julia Peterson
any longer, didn't want to learn the answers to her un-
spoken questions, didn't want to pursue a conversation
that revolved around Daniel. Out of the corner of her

eye she saw the white Rolls-Royce draw up outside the church gates and gratefully seized the chance for escape.

'Oh, it looks as if James and Robyn are just about to leave for the reception,' she said brightly. 'I'd better go and track down my brother and sister.' The jaw-aching smile fixed firmly in place, she turned away and collided with Daniel. He stretched out an automatic hand to steady her and she recoiled from his touch, taking an immediate step backward. For a brief second their eyes met, and she was shaken to see the expression of complete and utter indifference reflected in the tawny-golden depths as without a word he continued past her.

Momentarily oblivious of her surroundings, Katherine came to an abrupt halt. Daniel deliberately antagonised her, taunted her with caustic gibes—he never simply ignored her! He might not like her, but she'd always evoked a positive response from him, he'd always been aware of her. Slowly she continued across the grass, absently searching for two familiar heads among the small crowd gathered by the entrance to the churchyard. That indifference she'd just witnessed in Daniel's eyes had to be contrived, couldn't possibly be genuine. Damn it all, how dared he simply look through her as if she were a total stranger? Three nights ago he'd held her in his arms, she'd entrusted him with a confidence...he couldn't simply pretend she no longer even existed!

She spotted the twins and moved towards them. Her confidence in her ability to get through this traumatic day with complete outward composure was fading rapidly. She felt tense and edgy, wound up as a coiled spring. And she'd only just dealt with the first hurdle of the day, she reminded herself gloomily. The worse ordeal, the moment she most dreaded, was yet to come.

* * *

Katherine entered the foyer of the plush hotel and joined the line of wedding guests waiting to be received into the room beyond. She shook hands and exchanged platitudes with Robyn's parents and then moved on.

'Katherine, how delightful you look.' James's mother greeted her warmly and bent to kiss her cheek. Somehow Katherine managed to smile back, and with horror registered the deep compassion in the older woman's eyes. Oh, God, what a fool she'd been to suppose that she always managed to conceal her feelings for James. There must have been so many times when she'd given herself away...a fleeting expression in her eyes, a nuance in her voice. Summoning every ounce of will-power, she turned towards the bride and groom and smiled.

'Robyn, you look beautiful,' she said glibly and looked up at James, studiously avoiding his eyes. 'Congratulations, James.' She was amazed at how calm and controlled her voice sounded. Casually she bestowed a quick, impersonal peck on his cheek and turned away.

It was over. She took a drink from a passing waiter and drank it in almost one gulp without even tasting it.

'All right, Kat?'

Her eyes focused on her brother. Was that a purely rhetorical question, or did Tim have some inkling of what she'd just gone through? Her eyes flickered to Jessica, standing by his side, and winced inwardly. Had the twins also guessed at her true feelings for James?

'It's very close in here,' she murmured vaguely. 'I think I'll go and freshen up.'

'We're going to wait for starter's orders,' Tim grinned, eyeing the lavish buffet displayed on white linen-covered tables in an alcove at the far end of the room.

Leaving the twins behind her, Katherine headed towards the powder-room. Was she being over-sensitive, imagining those quick sideways glances of sympathy and curiosity that she seemed to be attracting? She had known most of the people present here today all her life; they would all be aware of her lifelong friendship with James. She had been naïve not to have realised before now that it was inevitable that there would have been a certain amount of speculation about the exact nature of that friendship.

'Katherine, my dear.'

A great-aunt of James's, renowned for her forthrightness, emerged from the powder-room just as she was about to enter, and greeted her with an unceremonious hug.

'I'm so glad you came today,' the elderly woman declared in a clear carrying voice. 'It must be so difficult for you.' She sighed. 'Robyn seems a pleasant enough girl, but I did always hope...'

Katherine's face fired with colour. This was getting unbearable. Why didn't she simply wear a placard around her neck proclaiming her unrequited love for James and have done with it? Muttering something inaudible under her breath, she bolted into the powder-room, relieved to find it deserted, and, leaning over a basin, splashed cold water on to her face. It was oddly touching as well as acutely embarrassing to be the recipient of so much sympathy today, even though that well-meaning sympathy was totally misplaced. Because she was no longer in love with James.

She dried her face on a towel and sat down on a velvet-covered stool, gazing thoughtfully at her reflection. There was no expression of shock in those calm green eyes, merely an acceptance of something she had guessed at several days ago and yet for some unaccountable reason had refused to admit until now. Why had it taken her

so long to recognise that the warm affection she felt for
James was exactly that and no more, and what had
finally prompted this revelation?

The door of the powder-room opened, and Katherine
fished in her clutch bag for a comb and ran it through
the length of her hair, sweeping the silky corn-coloured
tresses back over her shoulder. She'd had the same hair-
style for years, she mused absently. Wasn't it about time
she thought about changing it? Perhaps she should ex-
periment not only with the style, but the colour...
brunette, for example? However did that absurd notion
infiltrate into her head? Swiftly she applied a pink gloss
to her lips, blotted them carefully with a tissue and stood
up, surveying herself quickly in the full-length wall
mirror. Accustomed to seeing herself in faded old jeans,
she couldn't quite relate to the poised, elegant-looking
girl in the pink silk dress, and pulled a face at her reflection just to confirm it was actually her. Then slowly
her mouth curved in a wide grin. She wasn't in love with
James or anyone else. She was free...emotionally intact.
It was an exhilarating, wonderful feeling.

'Wine?'

Katherine shook her head and the stocky dark-haired
young man beside her refilled his own glass and replaced
the bottle back on the table in front of him. Except for
the glass of sherry when she'd arrived, she'd confined
herself to soft drinks. She felt elated and light-headed
enough already, and certainly didn't need any further
stimulant.

'So,' her companion of the last ten minutes grinned
at her engagingly, 'no husband, fiancé, boyfriend or
lover.'

She shook her head, grinning back. Even before he had introduced himself, she had guessed that the young man was Robyn's brother, the family likeness very apparent. The attractive accent in his voice had confirmed it.

'Well, I simply don't understand what's wrong with these English guys.'

It had been a long time since she'd witnessed such undisguised interest in male eyes, Katherine realised. That Rick was by nature an outrageous flirt and not to be taken seriously she didn't doubt for a second. But he was entertaining and fun to be with and his frivolous, light-hearted conversation was exactly attuned to her own mood.

'Thank you.' She smiled as a hovering waiter handed her a fluted glass and then filled it with champagne. An expectant hush fell over the room as Robyn's father rose to his feet, made a short speech and toasted the bride and groom.

'Robyn and James,' Katherine murmured, taking a sip from her glass, her eyes warm with affection as they rested on the groom. He was the best friend she'd ever had, she thought with a rush of sentiment, and nothing would ever alter that fact.

'James seems like a really nice guy.'

'He is,' Katherine murmured quietly, and smiled at the sudden realisation that the man beside her was now James's brother-in-law.

'Now that is a much more complex guy,' he observed as Daniel rose to his feet. 'I should guess that it takes a long while to figure out what makes him tick.'

Katherine shrugged, eyes dropping to the table, refusing to look at Daniel, closing her mind to the familiar, deep voice. He'd performed his duties as best man admirably this afternoon, she thought caustically. With Julia in tow, he'd circulated among the guests, topping up empty glasses, ensuring that elderly relatives were seated comfortably and plentifully supplied from the excellent buffet. He'd exchanged pleasantries with virtually everyone in the room—the one notable exception being her. Just once she'd caught him watching her. She'd been laughing at some comment of Rick's and had glanced up to find Daniel's eyes resting on her, lines of grim disapproval etched on his face, and had wondered with a brief surge of irritation what she'd done to merit such silent condemnation.

The sound of laughter and spontaneous applause echoed around the room. Evidently Daniel's speech had been a good one. The wedding cake was cut and distributed, while in the background a small band began to play slow, romantic melodies.

The bride and groom moved on to the small dance-floor at the far end of the room and after an interval were joined by other couples. With amusement Katherine spotted Tim, an expression of unconcealed horror on his face, being shunted across the floor in the arms of a large, forceful woman. Her eyes moved over the other couples and focused on a rapturous-looking Jessica, dancing with Daniel. So Daniel wasn't ignoring the Maitland family *en masse*; she alone had been selected for the privilege. His attitude towards her today had been utterly puerile, she thought witheringly.

'Would you like to dance?'

'I'd love to,' Katherine responded brightly, but the enthusiasm in her voice was as contrived as the smile on her face.

She allowed Rick to lead her on to the floor and made no protest when he drew her against him as they moved together in time the slow beat. It was odd, she reflected, that she could be so close to this undeniably attractive young man and feel nothing. Daniel came into her line of vision, Julia now nestled into the curve of his arms, and with a clarity that shook her Katherine recalled exactly how it felt to be held in those arms. She was nearly caught off guard as Daniel suddenly glanced sideways towards her, and instantly she directed her gaze at Rick, smiling warmly up into his eyes, laughing uproariously as he murmured something in her ear, although it had been completely inaudible.

The tempo of the music increased and Katherine attempted to match the complicated steps of her partner, but her energy seemed to be waning.

'I could sure do with a drink,' Rick announced, much to her relief, and she followed him across to the bar. She lifted the thick mane of hair from her neck, but the air in the room was too warm to have much effect on her heated skin. She took a long, grateful sip from the iced tonic water she'd requested and stood with her back to the bar, surveying the room. Robyn and James had disappeared, presumably to change into less formal attire. The twins were sitting at a table, chatting to two young cousins of James's, Coke bottles strewn around them. With a jolt of irritation she realised that she was quite deliberately searching for a familiar russet head. Surely Daniel hadn't left already? She was aware that the newlyweds were booked into the hotel bridal suite for the night and that Daniel was due to drive them to the airport in the morning to catch their flight to Crete. Perhaps Julia and Daniel were also booked in the hotel for the night? Oh, for Pete's sake, it was simply no concern of hers.

Rick was chatting to the bar attendant, and it occurred to her for the first time that his speech was becoming slightly slurred. That large whisky in his hand wasn't going to help matters, she observed drily.

'I think I'll just pop outside for some fresh air,' she murmured casually, and, glass in her hand, wandered through the room towards the open french windows, grateful that Rick made no attempt to follow her. She stepped outside and faltered as she saw that the terrace was already occupied.

Daniel, his shoulders hunched, hands in the pockets of his trousers, was staring out over the hotel grounds and seemed completely oblivious to her presence. Warily she took a silent step towards him and came to an abrupt halt, shaken by the bleakness on his face.

She'd never in all her life seen Daniel look like this. His slumped posture, that awful, chilling emptiness on his face . . . he looked so defeated. That was the very last word she would have ever dreamed of using in context with Daniel and yet right now it was the only one that applied. What on earth was the matter with him? Had today sparked off memories of his own wedding? she suddenly wondered, and then quickly dismissed the idea. Why did she always find it so difficult to attribute emotions and feelings to Daniel that she would find perfectly normal in other people?

She surveyed him with dark, cautious eyes, certain that if she approached him he would rebuff her. The wisest course of action would be to beat a hasty retreat. She turned round, the heel of her shoe caught in a crack in the paving and she slipped over, miraculously managing to keep hold of her glass. So much for a silent exit, she thought ruefully, scrambling to her feet. Still, at least there was no damage done, except to her dignity. Damn it all, Daniel could at least ask if she was all right, instead of standing there, surveying her as if she were something that had crawled out from underneath the nearest stone.

His gaze moved from her flushed, heated face and rested on the glass she was still clutching in her hand.

'Don't you think you have had more than enough of that?' he demanded contemptuously. 'It's not going to solve anything.'

'For heaven's sake, Daniel,' she snapped witheringly as she absorbed the implication of his words. What did he think her glass contained? Neat gin? 'I'm only drinking... Daniel!' Her voice rose with exasperation as, without waiting for her to finish, he turned and strode back through the french windows. She began to follow and then stopped abruptly. She didn't have to justify herself to Daniel. If he chose to believe that she was intent on drinking herself into a state of oblivion, presumably to forget James, let him.

Shrugging, she took a sip from the innocuous contents of her glass and watched the shadows creeping across the hotel grounds. She wished she could recapture her earlier mood of elation and well-being, but it seemed to have disintegrated completely. She felt flat, empty. But wasn't that inevitable? she mused. It might be a relief to discover that she was no longer in love with James, but he had occupied so much of her thoughts over the past few years that she was bound to be left with a void in her life for a while. Recognising her own perverseness, she grinned. Loving James hadn't brought her any happiness, and now she was feeling depressed because she *didn't* love him! No, not depressed. Frightened. And vulnerable. Her expression sobered and, despite the warmth of the evening, goose-bumps tingled down her bare arm. She was being utterly ridiculous, she chided herself irritably. There was nothing to fear from the future.

'There you are. I thought you'd deserted me.'

Collecting herself quickly, Katherine turned round and smiled automatically at Rick. The slur in his voice was even more pronounced and as he moved towards her she could smell the harsh smell of whisky on his breath.

'Come on.' He grabbed hold of her free hand. 'Let's dance again.'

Gently Katherine eased her hand from his clasp. 'I think I'll stay out here for a while longer,' she murmured casually, and groaned inwardly as he placed an arm across her shoulder, drew her towards him and looked down at her with heavy, glazed eyes. The last thing she wanted was to be involved in an unpleasant scene with the bride's brother.

'Rick...' she began firmly, and recoiled with distaste as his mouth covered hers in a moist, urgent kiss. Her strenuous efforts to push him away were ineffectual and she moved her hands from his shoulders and reached up to the back of his head. Whether he was brother of the bride or not, a sharp, painful tug of his hair should cool his alcohol-induced ardour.

'I believe Robyn is looking for you.'

Katherine went rigid, her fingers locked into Rick's hair as over his shoulder she saw Daniel looming towards them. She saw the disdain on his face, and for a second viewed the scene as if through his eyes... saw her fingers apparently curled caressingly through Rick's hair as she stood entwined in his arms.

Her hands dropped to her side, and as Rick's hold relaxed she wrenched herself free from his embrace. To her incredulity he grinned down at her and touched her cheek with his hand.

'Don't go away,' he murmured. 'Shan't be long. Just see what Robyn wants.' Whistling cheerfully, he walked unsteadily across the terrace towards the french windows.

Katherine watched him disappear into the room beyond and shrugged dismissively. The momentary anger she'd experienced had vanished. She couldn't get hysterical about a brief, albeit unwanted kiss from a man who'd drunk too much on his sister's wedding-day, although she would have preferred not to have had the episode witnessed. How had Daniel just happened to appear at that precise moment? she wondered, shooting him a quick, speculative glance.

'Don't let me detain you, now that you've run your errand for Robyn,' she murmured sweetly, stung by his silent, contemptuous appraisal. Considering his own record with women, he was hardly in a position to be so sanctimonious about a mere kiss. And at least Rick had kissed her because he found her attractive; he hadn't simply been indulging in some egotistical power game. The muscles in her stomach tightened.

'Well, it's been delightful chatting to you.' Smiling brilliantly, she began to saunter casually across the terrace.

'Does Rick know he's simply consolation prize, or are you planning to tell him in the morning? What are you going to do? Close your eyes and pretend it's your wedding-night with James?'

Katherine halted, her back stiffening as she heard the taunting voice behind her. So she had managed to dent Daniel's male ego the other night! That cheap crack about Rick proved it. A few minutes ago Daniel had virtually accused her of being drunk, and now he was implying that she was proposing to leap into bed with a virtual stranger. She took a deep breath, squashing the swirl of disgust and anger rising up inside her. Daniel was deliberately trying to provoke her, goad her into losing her temper, and it wasn't going to work. She wasn't going to retaliate, wasn't going to get involved in some childish slanging match. She was simply going to ignore him and walk away...

'Ouch!' She yelped her protest as Daniel caught hold of her arm and swung her round to face him.

'My God, if you couldn't manage to get through today with some modicum of dignity, why did you bother to come?' He towered above her, raking her face with narrowed eyes. 'Haven't you any pride?'

It took every ounce of control to keep her expression impassive, but somehow Katherine managed it. 'Would you mind letting go of my arm?' she said evenly. 'You're hurting me!' Her voice rose as, far from releasing her, his hold tightened and he drew her roughly towards him. With his free hand he cupped her chin, tilting her face up towards him.

'What's my name?' The soft drawl in his voice was totally belied by the ominous glint in his eyes.

'Don't be ridiculous,' Katherine muttered, fighting back the surge of panic.

'You haven't answered my question.' Casually he began to trace the contour of her lower lip with his thumb.

The colour rose and ebbed in Katherine's face. Daniel's hand had dropped from her arm. She could move away from him at any time she chose. Except that her legs wouldn't seem to obey her command. She seemed to be totally immobilised, transfixed, imprisoned in some alien force field.

'Look at me, Katherine.'

Slowly her eyes travelled over the strong, rugged planes of his face, dropped to the square, uncompromising jaw and came to rest on the firm, straight mouth, now barely inches away from her own. She felt light-headed, could hear the blood pounding in her ears, was aware of nothing but that searing ache inside her...

No! She recoiled backwards as the word screamed in her head. She knew exactly what Daniel was playing at and she wasn't going to fall into another of his humiliating traps. Her instinct was simply to turn and flee, put as much distance between herself and Daniel as possible, but instead, calling on every ounce of will-power in her body, she stood her ground and surveyed Daniel equably.

'Won't Julia be wondering where you are?' she enquired with sugary innocence, amazed at how steady and controlled her voice sounded. Not waiting for a response, she began to walk nonchalantly towards the french windows and then changed direction, descending the few wide steps from the terrace into the hotel grounds. She couldn't face anyone just yet, needed desperately to be on her own for a while until that pounding in her chest subsided and her pulse-rate returned to normal.

Walking briskly, she followed a gravel path, bordered by immaculate flowerbeds, that led towards a small ornamental lake set amid a small copse of trees which offered the privacy and seclusion she craved.

Why did she allow Daniel to disturb her so much? she wondered bitterly, coming to a halt at the edge of the lake and staring down into the still water. Grimacing, she cringed inwardly, burning with self-disgust as she recalled how for a few insane moments she had wanted, more than anything in the world, to feel Daniel's arms around her, to taste his mouth against hers. God, she was so weak, so appallingly shallow, to let herself become such an easy prey to the most basic of instincts, attracted to a man not because she was emotionally drawn towards him, but purely because her traitorous body found him physically desirable.

She stooped down, picked up a pebble and hurled it ferociously into the lake. She loathed Daniel Sinclair. But not as much as she loathed herself right now. Needing to expend that furious, restless energy inside of her before she exploded, she marched rapidly around the lake, and then flung herself down on a wooden bench set conveniently alongside the water's edge.

Today was evidently the day for self-revelation, so why wasn't she completely honest with herself, something she should have been years ago? Admitting the exact nature of her feelings for James was only the halfway stage. She stared reflectively into space and finally drew a deep breath.

At the age of seventeen she had believed herself to be in love. Not with her childhood friend James. But with Daniel.

CHAPTER FIVE

KATHERINE slumped back on the bench and sighed, a feeling of overwhelming relief flooding her as she finally came to terms with the truth after so many years of deliberate self-delusion. Closing her eyes, she forced her thoughts back over the years, determined for once to view the past with complete honesty.

As a child, she admitted, she had frankly adored Daniel. He had teased her unmercifully, she remembered, but she'd never minded, has just been gratified that the object of her secret hero-worship had even noticed her. Of course, after the accident everything had changed . . . Daniel had changed. He had stopped teasing her, stopped looking at her with that expression of warm amusement in his eyes, and she had known then that he would always blame her for destroying his dream of becoming a professional tennis player. She had been like a lost, confused puppy that long-ago summer, as she had tried desperately hard to ingratiate herself back into favour with her idol. But the more she had tried to please him, the more irritable he had become. Hurt and bewildered, unable to deal with the impossible burden of guilt, she had found it simpler to just block Daniel and the accident from her mind completely. As she grew into her teens it became second nature to avoid Daniel whenever possible, to close her ears if anyone mentioned his name in her hearing. On the rare occasions that she did encounter him, she treated him with the careful, uninterested politeness she would have accorded a total stranger and escaped his presence as quickly as possible. Quite simply, she had tried to erase Daniel Sinclair from her life. That was why it had been such an appalling shock...

Katherine opened her eyes and looked unseeingly into the distance as the memories unfurled in her head. The New Year's Eve party at the Sinclairs' shortly after her seventeenth birthday... A sudden hush as someone switched on the radio and the chimes of Big Ben echoed around the crowded room. Midnight. Quite by chance she had been standing next to Daniel and he'd kissed her...

Katherine smiled wryly. In retrospect, all Daniel had done was place his hands on her shoulders and lightly brush her lips with his mouth. But even now she could recall those terrifying, bewildering emotions that the casual kiss had unleashed. With the wisdom of hindsight, what she'd actually experienced that night were the first stirrings of sexual attraction for a man. But of course the immature, romantic, adolescent Katherine hadn't been able to view it in such basic terms and had decided that she had fallen in love with Daniel... fallen in love with a man who hated her, who could hardly stand even to be in the same room as her!

Katherine grinned, embarrassed at the memory of her teenage self. How could she have ever been quite so naïve? But even now she could recall that sense of shocked outrage that had engulfed her as she'd railed at the unfairness of life. Those new and disturbing feelings curdling deep inside of her should have been aroused by James... not by Daniel. What if Daniel should ever suspect even for a moment how she felt about him? That was when the deception with James had started. She had started to use him like a shield, protecting herself from

Daniel, and in the end she'd actually convinced herself that she was in love with him.

Or had she? Hadn't she deep down in her subconscious always known the truth? It hadn't been James's imminent wedding that had caused her so many sleepless nights over the past few months but the realisation that she would be seeing Daniel again. The afternoon she had gone to James's cottage, and Daniel had opened the door to her, all her fears had been realised. After Daniel's absence of two years that pull of physical attraction she'd tried so desperately hard to deny had merely intensified. And even then, when the truth was staring at her in the face, she'd still refused to acknowledge it openly, still persisted in her subterfuge with James.

Slowly Katherine rose to her feet. She was physically drawn to a man who repelled her emotionally, and there didn't seem to be a damn thing she could do about it. But at least finally accepting that unpalatable fact was half the battle. Knowing how vulnerable she was, she would simply make a concerted effort to avoid Daniel at all cost. It wasn't as if their paths were likely to cross that often, anyway, even though he was now presumably going to be a neighbour. Her expression resolute, she took a deep breath and began to walk purposefully back towards the hotel.

Katherine glanced up from the lettuce she was rinsing in the kitchen sink as the twins trooped through the back door. Judging from the number of plastic bags they were carrying, their shopping expedition on the bus to Salisbury for new jeans and T-shirts had been a successful one.

'That was well timed,' she grinned at them. 'I'm just about to get lunch.'

'We've already had some,' Jessica informed her, diving into her shopping bag. 'What do you think of this? It was reduced.'

'Should suit you,' Katherine murmured, and with great restraint refused to point out that the summer skirt being paraded wasn't the pair of jeans Jessica had apparently so desperately needed that morning. 'What did you have for lunch? Beefburger?'

'No.' Tim produced two identical blue T-shirts for inspection. 'We met Daniel in Salisbury and he offered us a lift home.'

'And then he asked us back for lunch at Norrington Hall,' Jessica chipped in.

'Oh, I see.' Katherine concentrated on washing the lettuce. She hadn't experienced the slightest pang of concern on learning that the twins had been passengers in Daniel's car, she realised. Perhaps she had finally come to terms with that particular nightmare. 'So Daniel's actually moved in now?' she asked casually. It certainly hadn't taken him long, she mused. It was barely a month since James's wedding.

'Mmm.' Jessica perched herself on the edge of the kitchen table. 'He's had the swimming-pool cleaned and mended and says we can use it any time we like. Which will be great if this heat wave continues.' She paused. 'And he's had the stables renovated and bought two horses.'

Alerted by the deceptive nonchalance that had crept into her sister's voice, Katherine flicked her an enquiring glance.

'Oh, Kat.' Jessica jumped to her feet, her face alight with excitement. 'Daniel's offered me a job looking after the horses. Starting tomorrow.'

Katherine swung back towards the sink. When the local riding school had been unable to offer Jessica anything more than the occasional free ride in return for her assistance she had believed that the battle for further education had finally been won. And now Daniel had to go and do this. He was fully aware of how she felt about Jessica's studying for her A levels . . .

'Isn't he terrific?'

'Wonderful,' Katherine agreed drily, screwing up the lettuce leaf in her hand. Damn Daniel Sinclair. If she refused to let Jessica take him up on his offer she was immediately going to be cast in the role of villain, which didn't augur well for the peaceful summer she'd been anticipating.

'And guess what else?' It was Tim's turn to look elated. 'Daniel knows a vet who runs a large animal practice over in Salisbury and he's going to ask him if I can go out on his rounds with him over the holidays.'

'Well, you have both had a productive morning,' Katherine muttered. She'd been relying on Tim's assistance in the garden over the summer months.

'Of course, I'll still be able to help you in the evenings,' Tim continued as if reading her mind, immediately making her feel guilty. It was a wonderful opportunity for Tim, she admitted. But she just heartily wished that it hadn't been Daniel in possession of the magic wand.

The twins, talking animatedly, retreated upstairs to change into shorts, and Katherine slung the lettuce into a colander, the salad she'd been proposing to have for lunch now singularly unappealing. Pushing her bare feet into a pair of canvas shoes, she went out of the back door to the wild garden at the side of the house, and sat cross-legged on the grass under the old apple tree, her favourite brooding place.

Automatically her eyes were drawn in the direction of Norrington Hall, the roof of the house just visible above the massive oak trees that dotted the parkland surrounding it. Her fair eyebrows knit together across her forehead. What possible long-term future was there for Jessica in working as a groom for Daniel? If her younger sister seriously wanted to spend her life working with horses of course she couldn't stand in her way—after Jessica had obtained some further academic qualifications on which to fall back later if necessary. Surely that wasn't unreasonable, simply common sense?

There seemed to be no alternative—she would have to go and see Daniel and insist that he withdraw his job offer to Jessica. Abruptly she jumped to her feet. And now seemed as good a time as any to tackle him when she could at least be sure he was alone, the twins having made no mention of anyone else present during their lunch. Darting back around the house, she stuck her head through the kitchen door.

'Just going out for a while,' she yelled and rushed out before she could be interrogated too closely. She scrambled over the wooden fence that separated the two adjoining properties, deciding to take the short cut to Norrington Hall across the park.

The weeks without rain were beginning to have effect. The once luxurious grass was brown and scorched, the ground beneath her feet rock-hard. Katherine glanced up at the azure sky and sighed. No rain cloud in sight. It was rumoured that a hose-pipe ban was shortly to be imposed on domestic users; heaven knew what she would do if water was restricted for commercial use as well.

The sun beat down on her bare head and she could feel a trickle of perspiration run down her face. She should have waited until it was cooler before charging over to see Daniel. Except if she had waited too long she would probably have lost her nerve, she admitted. It was ridiculous to feel so apprehensive about seeing him again but, as Norrington Hall loomed closer in front of her, she could feel the adrenalin begin to pump through her body. She hadn't seen Daniel since her encounter with him on the hotel terrace at James's wedding and wasn't quite certain how she was going to react when she did so. But whatever happened, she thought determinedly, she was going to remain cool and composed—at least outwardly, she added with a wry grin. She was going to discuss Jessica calmly and rationally, without losing her temper.

She opened a gate as she came to the far end of the park and began to walk up the long drive towards the house. What a mess she must look, clad in her tatty cut-off jeans and an old T-shirt of Tim's, with her hair tied back from her face in a pony-tail. It had crossed her mind to change, perhaps into a summer dress, but some perverseness deep inside her had rebelled at the thought that she was deliberately trying to make herself look attractive for Daniel.

Taking a deep breath, she mounted the wide steps leading up to the solid front door and rang the bell. What on earth did Daniel need a house this size for? she wondered, taking a step back and staring up at the imposing, elegant house. It was far too big for one person. She shrugged. But then perhaps Daniel wasn't planning to live here alone...

She frowned and rang the bell again. The door remained firmly shut and she gazed at it uncertainly. Daniel must be in; his car was parked in the gravel crescent sweep in front of the house.

'Hello, Katherine.'

She started as she heard the deep voice behind her and swung round, her breath catching in her throat at the sight of Daniel, apparently clad in nothing but a white towel knotted around his waist.

'I was just about to have a swim,' he drawled. 'Come on round to the back.'

Katherine nodded wordlessly, keeping her eyes firmly ahead of her as she walked by his side. But the image of bronzed, powerful shoulders had already been imprinted into her mind. She registered, too, that Daniel had evinced no surprise at her appearance. He'd probably been expecting her, had known that she would come charging over as soon as Jessica relayed the news of her job offer. He'd once accused her of being predictable, she remembered—and it would appear that he was right.

Despite her tension, she began to look around her curiously as she was guided through what presumably had once been a kitchen garden, now overgrown and neglected, along a paved path bordered on each side by rose beds suffocated with weeds. Over to the left stretched a lawn, merging into a wilderness that had once been a shrubbery. She would adore to get her hands on this garden and restore it to its former glory, Katherine thought with a pang of wistfulness. There was something so sad and pathetic about seeing a once lovingly tended garden reduced to this state of neglect.

Without thinking, she stooped down and started to pull vigorously at some bindweed and then, realising what she was doing, stood up self-consciously, her discomfort increasing as she saw Daniel standing a few paces ahead, arms folded across his chest, watching her.

'It's a mess,' she announced defiantly, tossing the bindweed aside.

'I've advertised for a full-time gardener,' he murmured as she reached his side and they continued along the path. 'But of course do feel free to come over any time with your fork and spade,' he added obligingly.

Her face tightened. It wouldn't hurt him to get down to some hard work in the garden instead of lolling about indolently by the pool all afternoon, she thought sourly. Her first priority would have been to get the garden in some sort of order; she wouldn't have been unduly concerned about the pool or stables. She wasn't even aware that Daniel could ride, come to think of it. It was odd, she reflected suddenly, that she had been acquainted with Daniel all her life and yet really, when it came down to it, she knew nothing about him at all.

'Thomas! What on earth are you doing here?' she demanded in disbelief as they reached the pool and she spotted the ginger cat stretched out lazily beneath a deck-chair. It was irritating enough to know that the twins had fallen under Daniel's spell, but to discover her faithless feline happily ensconced in the enemy camp was the last straw. To compound matters, the ginger tom scrambled to its paws, and, ignoring her disdainfully, started to rub itself around Daniel's legs, purring ferociously.

'He started to appear a couple of days ago,' Daniel murmured idly, sitting down on a deck-chair.

'And you made him a job offer he couldn't refuse. Chief mouser in return for a staple diet of fresh salmon and turkey,' Katherine returned waspishly, selecting an upright wicker chair.

Daniel quirked a dark eyebrow. 'Jessica?' he enquired laconically.

Full marks for perception, Katherine thought acidly.

'You shouldn't have mentioned anything to her without discussing it with me first. You knew exactly how I felt about...' Katherine heard the rising anger in her voice and shut her mouth abruptly. She'd vowed to keep her temper and already she was flaring up. But the anger curdling inside her wasn't anything to do with her indignation about Jessica, she realised uneasily. She was angry with Daniel because of the disturbing effect his proximity was having upon her. She didn't want to feel this way, hated the dipping sensation in the pit of her stomach every time she looked at him. She didn't even have to look at him! The air around her seemed to be suffused by his maleness. That truth session on James's wedding-day had been an appalling mistake, she thought regretfully. How much better to have continued in blissful ignorance, believing herself to be completely immune to Daniel.

She cleared her throat and tried again. 'I should be grateful if you would tell Jessica that you've changed your mind,' she murmured with calm formality.

'But I haven't,' he murmured with an infuriating smile. 'And surely Jessica is old enough to make some decisions for herself without having to rush to you for approval. Besides which, I really can't see why you object so strongly anyway.'

'You can't see why I object to seeing my sister making the biggest mistake of her life?' Katherine shook her head in disbelief. 'Why the hell did you have to interfere anyway?' she demanded. Jessica had just about become resigned to enrolling for college in September, and now Daniel had to upset everything. 'You're the most thoughtless, inconsiderate...' Abruptly she rose to her feet. What was the point of wasting any more of her time trying to talk to Daniel? She would get more response conversing with a brick wall.

'Do you wear a sun hat when you're working outside?'

'What?' Katherine was thrown off balance by the sudden, seemingly totally irrelevant question.

'It was just a thought,' Daniel murmured mildly. 'Too much sun can have the strangest effect on some people. Makes them irrational, prone to bouts of bad temper, hysteria...'

'How fascinating. And of course you're absolutely right. It's totally irrational for me to be concerned about Jessica's future.'

'Oh, for Pete's sake, Katherine, stop stamping about like an irate grasshopper and sit down.'

Grasshopper. The pet name Daniel had bestowed upon her as a child because she'd been so much tinier than both him and James. Had he used it deliberately to disconcert her, or had his choice of simile been totally unconscious?

'I've asked Jessica if she'd like to help out with the horses over the school holiday. That's all.'

Slowly Katherine slumped back down into her chair. 'I thought...when Jesse said that you'd offered her a job I just assumed it was permanent.'

'So I gather,' Daniel murmured drily.

'Well, you could have told me earlier. You must have realised what I was thinking...' Katherine mumbled grudgingly, unconsciously tracing a circle on the ground with her foot.

'And you could have checked your facts with Jessica first.'

'Yes,' Katherine admitted, sighing inwardly. Oh, well, things could have been worse, she thought philosophically. At least she had kept her temper in check and had been reasonably restrained and dignified. She supposed she now owed him an apology of some sort. Cautiously she flicked him a glance from under her lashes and frowned. He was sprawled back in his chair with his eyes closed.

She swallowed convulsively as her gaze moved over the broad golden shoulders and followed the line of fine dark hair that covered the deep chest and disappeared beneath the towel. Hell's bells, she felt like a voyeur, she thought with a rise of disgust.

'Daniel!' she said sharply.

Lazily he opened his eyes and stretched his arms above his head, the movement causing the towel to fall aside, revealing black swimming trunks beneath. But it wasn't the powerful thighs that caught Katherine's attention; her eyes were drawn like a magnet to puckered scar running down the inside of his right leg. For one long second she was mesmerised, unable to look away, and then, flinching, she turned her head aside, feeling sick.

She'd certainly left her mark on Daniel, she thought with mounting hysteria. He would remember her for the rest of his life. The familiar conflict began to rage inside her. Guilt for the unthinking, reckless action of a ten-year-old child who had destroyed a man's dreams. And anger directed at Daniel for not having granted the so desperately needed absolution to that child.

If only he would talk to her about the accident, Katherine thought with frustration. Surely it would be beneficial to both of them to finally confront the issue, and openly admit to their respective anger and resentment? She winced. Be honest. All she really wanted, had ever wanted, was for Daniel to say that he forgave her.

'Daniel…don't you think…?' The words died on her lips as she turned her head towards him and saw the cold, unresponsive expression on his face. He knew what she had been about to say and wasn't interested. With a jolt of unease she saw that he had pulled the towel back over his legs, an action, she was convinced, that hadn't been prompted by a sudden rush of modesty, but to conceal the scar. Was he self-conscious about it? she wondered. And then the truth hit her. That harshness in his eyes… He thought she'd been repulsed by the scar, hadn't understood that it had been that tearing pain inside her that had made her flinch and look away…

She heard him scrape back his chair and watched with shadowed eyes as, wordlessly, he strode to the edge of the pool, tossed his towel aside and dived in. He pounded through the water, executed a perfect tumble turn at the far end and powered his way back down the pool. Coming to a halt, he rested his elbows on the edge of the pool and looked up at Katherine.

'Come on in,' he drawled.

'Dressed like this?' She felt bewildered by his rapid mood change, unsettled by the lazy, teasing grin. She ought to go home right now, a small voice in her head instructed her. She'd only come over to Norrington Hall to discuss Jessica, and now that had been accomplished there was no reason for her to remain any longer.

'There's a costume in the changing-room that should be about your size.'

Katherine hesitated. The shimmering blue water did look enticing. After all, she reasoned, wasn't she being a little paranoid about Daniel? What possible harm could there be in going for a quick swim in a neighbour's swimming-pool, which, when it came down to it, was all she would be doing?

'All right. Thanks,' she murmured casually, and made her way around the edge of the pool to the red-brick changing-room.

She began to strip off her clothes and then paused, as out of the corner of her eye she glimpsed the black swimsuit hanging up behind the door. Who did it belong to? Julia? She grimaced. She didn't want to use a costume that belonged to the other girl. So what did she do now? Put her clothes back on and tell Daniel she'd changed her mind? She stretched up a hand and lifted the costume from the hook to study it more closely, and grinned. Panic over. She couldn't visualise Julia or any other female with whom Daniel might be acquainted wearing this sensible, strictly functional one-piece. A much more likely candidate for ownership was Daniel's mother—who, Katherine was sure, wouldn't object to her borrowing it in the least.

Katherine slipped on the costume and, slightly ashamed of herself but unable to resist, stood up on a chair so that she could inspect her reflection in the half-length mirror on the wall. Not too bad. In fact, the severe style suited her better than a more ornate one would have. Katherine pulled a mocking face. She was going for a swim, not proposing to walk down a catwalk!

Emerging from the changing-room, she walked across to the pool and sat down on the edge, watching Daniel cut through the water with effortless ease. With his broad shoulders, narrow hips and long legs, he had the perfect physique for a swimmer. Unbidden, a lump formed in Katherine's throat. She'd never supposed that a man could be beautiful before, but that was the only word she could think of to describe the sleek, powerful male form.

Daniel came to a halt at the far end of the pool and pulled himself out. As he walked around the side towards her, droplets of water glistening on his shoulders and on the mat of dark hair on his chest, the sheer force of his attraction made her feel dizzy. Without waiting for him to reach her, she plunged into the water.

She should have listened to that warning voice in her head, she thought despairingly, and gone straight home. She'd vowed to avoid Daniel whenever possible and yet had seized on the very first excuse she could to come rushing over to see him. There had been no necessity to see him in person—she could have telephoned. In fact, if she'd waited and talked to Jessica there would have been no need to get into contact with him at all. So why had she deliberately placed herself in the danger zone? She came to the end of the pool, caught hold of the side and floated her legs out behind her. Because, she admitted reluctantly, over the past few weeks, for no accountable reason, she'd been uncharacteristically bored, filled with a lethargy that couldn't be contributed solely to the hot weather. And quite simply, whatever her reservations about Daniel, he always made her feel alive, charged with a new energy and self-awareness. Being with him was like standing on the edge of a precipice; one false step and she would be tumbling into the unknown. It was a sensation both terrifying and stimulating—but never boring. She was like a reckless child, she thought ruefully, wilfully drawn to danger because it was exciting. 'I must be insane!'

'Admitting it is supposed to be the first step, I believe,' Daniel drawled, swimming up behind her. Casually he flipped a quick somersault and came up beside her.

'Show-off,' Katherine murmured lightly, collecting herself quickly. She really ought to stop talking to herself out loud, a habit she seemed to have acquired since working on her own. 'I've never been able to do a tumble turn,' she confessed. 'I'm always scared I'll hit my head against the wall.'

Daniel trod water as he grinned into her face. 'Personal tuition always available. Negotiable terms. No hidden extras.'

Katherine's stomach muscles contracted. This Daniel with the laughing hazel-gold eyes was one she thought had vanished forever, and reminded her all too vividly of the boy he had once been. It was impossible not to respond to his wide grin, impossible to stop the warm glow seeping through her body.

'OK,' she smiled back at him, 'you teach me how to tumble turn without knocking myself senseless and I'll send you over a week's supply of vegetables.'

'Deal.' Daniel slapped the water in front of him with his hand and turned to her with mock solemnity. 'Now, then, Miss Maitland, if you'd like to pay attention, class is now in session.'

With assumed meekness Katherine listened to his instructions and then tried to implement them, choking with laughter as she bobbed up from the water after her first unsuccessful effort.

'You're not concentrating,' Daniel rebuked her severely as she repeated the manoeuvre several times. 'Try again.'

'You always were a hard task-master,' she protested, swimming back down the pool a few yards to position herself for her next attempt. Was he experiencing the same sense of *déjà vu*, remembering the hours he had spent patiently teaching her to swim as a child? It was years since she had felt this relaxed, this unconstrained in Daniel's company.

As he finally called a close to the lesson, breathless but triumphant, Katherine pulled herself out of the pool.

'Not bad at all,' Daniel commented, looking up at her from the water. 'A bit more practice and——'

'Not bad?' Katherine interjected with mock indignation. 'That last turn wouldn't have looked out of place at the Olympics!' She stepped back from the pool swiftly, avoiding the hand that snaked upwards towards her ankle, and, grinning over her shoulder, headed for the changing-room.

'Soap, shampoo and towels in the cupboard,' Daniel called after her retreating figure.

Katherine stripped off her swimsuit and stepped under the shower, humming under her breath as she soaped the scent of chlorine from her skin. She dried herself quickly on a huge, soft white towel and tugged on her clothes, and for no reason started to grin. Perhaps she really was going insane, she thought, bursting into laughter. She'd only learned how to execute a very basic tumble turn, for heaven's sake—and yet she was feeling as exhilarated as if she'd just climbed Everest!

Emerging back into the sunlight, she was momentarily disconcerted to discover the pool area deserted. Daniel had probably gone up to the house to change, she decided, stretching out comfortably on a lounger. Squeezing the water from her hair, she combed it with her fingers and spread it around her shoulders to dry.

'It's no good trying to get back into favour just because it's coming up to mealtime, you feckless feline,' she murmured severely as the ginger tom padded towards her, mewing throatily. How much longer was Daniel going to be? She sat up, shielding the sun from her eyes with a hand as she gazed up towards the house.

Perhaps he had just assumed she would join him up there when she was ready.

She swung her legs to the ground, jumped to her feet and began to head towards the house, cutting across the ill-kept lawn. Then, impulsively, she broke into a run, stretched her hands above her head and turned three cartwheels in rapid succession. Righting herself, she grinned up at the azure sky. Why did she suddenly feel so ridiculously happy? she wondered, shaking back her hair over her shoulder. She retrieved her sandals and continued across the lawn more sedately, coming to an abrupt halt as she turned the corner of the house.

Daniel, clad in a white towelling robe, arms folded across his chest, was standing beside Julia Peterson, his head inclined towards her as he listened intently to what she was saying. As if to emphasise some point, she laid a proprietorial hand on his arm, smiling as she looked up into his eyes. She was wearing a red halter-neck sundress, the colour a perfect foil for her dark hair, and her exposed skin was smooth and suntanned. Had Daniel been expecting Julia, Katherine wondered, or had the other girl arrived unexpectedly?

Transfixed, she watched as Daniel suddenly swept up Julia into his arms and swung her round in the air. 'Have I ever told you just how wonderful you are?' he drawled, laughing down into her face as he placed her back on the ground. He drew her towards him and kissed her soundly.

She shouldn't be standing here like this, watching them, Katherine thought with horror. Why hadn't she called out to Daniel as she'd approached, made him aware of her presence straight away? She wanted to avert her eyes, rush away undetected, but her legs wouldn't seem to function properly. And now it was too late to make her escape because Julia had seen her, was nudging Daniel.

'Hello, Julia.' Katherine sauntered towards them, smiling airily, hoping fervently that they would assume she had just arrived on the scene.

'Katherine.' The grin vanished from Daniel's face; his eyes were dark, unreadable. 'I'm sorry, I——'

'I'm just off,' she cut in quickly. She didn't want him to apologise, admit that he had simply forgotten her existence.

'Thanks for the lesson,' she added lightly. 'I'll send the vegetables over with Jesse in the morning.'

Daniel looked at her blankly for a second and then nodded. 'Right. Thanks.'

He hadn't even remembered their flippant bargain, Katherine realised. Neither had he suggested that she come over to use the pool again. She was evidently not to be included in the open invitation he had extended to the twins.

'Well, goodbye.' She could sense both Daniel and Julia willing her departure, felt like an unwelcome guest at a party. She turned away, uncomfortably aware of two pairs of eyes following her progress as she disappeared from view around the side of the house.

Hands sunk deep into the pockets of her shorts, she meandered slowly down the drive and paused as she came to the gate leading back into the park. Leaning against it, she stared into the distance. She didn't want to go home, didn't feel like preparing supper for the twins, didn't have the energy to do the watering and start crating up vegetables for the morning. She wanted . . . she didn't know what she wanted, couldn't understand that yearning deep inside her.

She opened the gate, walked through and closed it carefully behind her, studiously avoiding looking back towards Norrington Hall. How were Julia and Daniel going to spend the evening? Not slaving away in the garden, that was for sure. She shook herself mentally. What had brought on this mood of nauseating self-pity? A short time ago she'd felt on top of the world, as if she could achieve anything she set her mind to...so what had happened to change all that? Abruptly she broke into a jog. She didn't want to pursue this pointless self-analysis, didn't even want to think, wanted to make her mind a complete blank. If only she could get rid of that gnawing, twisted feeling deep inside of her...

CHAPTER SIX

KATHERINE jumped out of the van, and, fishing her key from the pocket of her jeans, let herself in through the front door. It was going to be another scorcher, she thought without enthusiasm, tugging off her dark green sweat-shirt and tossing it on to the hall table. Seven-thirty in the morning and already she was beginning to feel uncomfortably warm.

'Morning, Kat.' The twins looked up from the breakfast table as she walked into the kitchen.

'Jess, how many times do I have to ask you not to wear your riding boots in the house?' Katherine demanded, moving across the tiled floor and retrieving a cup and saucer from the cupboard. 'You're not a child. And for heaven's sake turn that radio off, Tim. I can hear it blaring out halfway down the lane. And don't read the newspaper while you're eating. I'm sick to death of finding it covered in marmalade.' She poured herself a cup of tea, grimacing as she took a mouthful. 'How long's this been made? It's stone-cold.'

'I'll make a fresh pot,' Tim said quietly, beginning to rise to his feet.

'Don't bother. I'll make a coffee.' Katherine switched on the kettle and leant back against the sink unit, waiting for it to boil. 'What time did you both get in last night?' she asked. Why did the twins look so subdued, so wary?

'Nineish,' Tim murmured. 'We tried to be quiet and not wake you.'

'Have a good time?' Katherine spooned instant coffee into a cup.

'Yes, thank you.'

Katherine surveyed Tim with a frown. He sounded so stiff, so formal. 'Who was there?' Why didn't she come straight out with it and ask if Julia Peterson had been among the guests at Norrington Hall last night?

'Mr and Mrs Sinclair, James, Robyn, all the usual,' Tim answered, leaving her no better informed. 'We gave Daniel your apologies. He's going to have another barbecue next Saturday and we're all invited again.'

Katherine raised her eyebrows. 'Pool parties, barbecues . . . how did we all manage to survive the weekend without dying of boredom before Daniel arrived on the scene to organise our social lives?'

'Why do you have to be so nasty about Daniel all the time?' Jessica glanced up from her bowl of cereal. 'Whenever either of us mentions his name, you always say something sarcastic. Well, I think it's great of him to keep inviting us over, and I don't know why you don't come occasionally. It might even cheer you up and——'

'Jesse . . .' Tim broke in warningly, but Jessica ignored him, her voice rising shrilly as she glared at Katherine.

'I'm getting fed up with it. All you ever do is snap our heads off these days. Everything we do is wrong.' She flung back her chair and stamped across to the door. 'I'm going to work.'

'She forgot her sandwiches,' Katherine mumbled as the door slammed shut, and then sank down in a chair, pressing her hands to her eyes. Swallowing hard, she raised her head and looked across at her brother. 'I'm sorry, Tim,' she said quietly. 'I know I've been . . .' She shrugged and raised her hands in a gesture of defeat.

How could she even begin to explain about those bursts of irrational anger that flooded her without warning, about those periods of aching loneliness that engulfed her, about that perpetual nagging emptiness inside her? She forced herself to smile. 'Better get a move on. Or you'll miss your bus.'

It hurt to see the expression of relief that flitted across Tim's face as he escaped from the kitchen—and from her. Jessica had been perfectly right, Katherine admitted unhappily. She'd been moody and tetchy for days now, jumping down the twins' throats practically every time they spoke, criticising everything they did. And it was time she snapped out of it, she told herself harshly.

Abruptly she scraped back her chair and began stacking the breakfast dishes in the sink. They could wait until later. She wanted to get as much done outside as she could before it got too hot. Then maybe this afternoon she'd go shopping and buy all the twins' favourite junk food for supper. It wouldn't hurt them for once. The sound of the front doorbell cut across her thoughts. Probably the milkman, she guessed. Armed with her purse, she went to open the door.

'Morning, Katherine.'

Before she'd had time to register what was happening Daniel had brushed by her and was walking down the hall towards the kitchen.

'I come bearing gifts,' he announced, indicating the carrier-bag in his hand. Whistling cheerfully, he produced an array of bottles, tubes and packets and set them out on the table.

'Cough mixture, throat pastilles, hay-fever tablets, insect repellent, antiseptic cream...' Katherine examined all the containers and then gave Daniel a dazzling smile. 'Let me guess: you've a new job—rep for a pharmaceutical company?'

Uninvited, Daniel sat down on a chair and stretched his legs out in front of him. 'Just concerned about your health,' he smiled back blandly. 'Let's see, last weekend you thought you were coming down with a summer cold…last night you had an appalling headache. So what are you going to be struck down with this weekend? Sore throat? Cough?' He shook his head. 'Tsh, tsh, I really thought you would be more inventive.'

Katherine shrugged, studying the tiled floor. There was no point in denying that her fictitious ailments had merely been excuses to refuse the invitations to Norrington Hall relayed to her via Jessica.

'Running away isn't going to solve anything. You're going to have to face up to it sooner or later.'

Katherine's head jerked up, her eyes dilating with sudden panic. Had Daniel guessed? 'I don't know what you're talking about.' There was a catch in her voice.

'Really?' He quirked an eyebrow at her. 'Does the name Robyn Sinclair ring any bells?' His voice deepened. 'You've got to finally accept that James is married, get used to seeing him with his wife.'

Katherine suppressed her sigh of relief. For one terrible moment she'd thought he had guessed the truth, that he had come over here to taunt her with the knowledge. If he believed that it was the thought of encountering Robyn and James that was deterring her from accepting his invitations to Norrington Hall she certainly wasn't going to disillusion him.

'Don't waste your life,' he continued quietly, 'wanting something that can never be yours.'

Katherine's face tightened as her eyes locked into his. Don't look at me like that, she yelled silently. Don't look at me as though you care. She'd seen that same warmth and gentleness on his face that afternoon in the swimming-pool. And it had meant nothing. The moment Julia Peterson had appeared he'd forgotten her entire existence.

'Thanks for the sermon,' she said acidly. How could anyone as astute as Daniel be so wide of the mark? 'And now I really must get on.' Pointedly she began to tug on her gardening gloves and slipped her feet into her shoes. She wasn't being very hospitable, she admitted, but she didn't have the time or inclination to sit around drinking coffee with Daniel. After all, she justified her ungraciousness, she hadn't invited him over this morning. In fact, if she had known it was him at the door she probably wouldn't have opened it.

'Why don't you go outside and have a good scream? It's supposed to be very therapeutic. Releases all that built-up anger and tension.' Unhurriedly Daniel rose to his feet and sauntered across the floor towards the back door.

'I'm not angry or tense,' Katherine snapped, her hands clenching into fists. 'I just happen to be extremely busy.'

'Don't scowl.' He turned round, blocking the doorway, surveying her with lazy golden eyes. 'You'll get lines on your forehead.'

'Goodbye, Daniel.' She waited expectantly for him to move out of the way so that she could pass through the door, and then, alerted by the expression on his face, she suddenly crouched down, pretending to refasten her shoes. She wasn't going to be subjected to any more of his meaningless farewell kisses.

'Be seeing you, Kat.'

She shrugged carelessly, irritated by both the amusement in his voice and his familiar use of the diminutive of her name, and waited until he had disappeared through the door before scrambling to her feet.

Why exactly had Daniel come round this morning? Mechanically she went outside to the shed, assembled her tools together and settled down to thin out a row of lettuce. She didn't for one moment believe that his visit had been prompted by concern for her welfare. Standing up, she moved to the next row, grateful for the slight breeze that seemed to have sprung up. All those bottles and tubes... he must have spent a fortune at the chemist's... Abruptly she sat back on her haunches, eyebrows knitting together. Why hadn't she laughed when Daniel had produced them from his bag, treated the whole thing as the joke it was intended to be? Why did she always look for some devious motive behind Daniel's every action, always wanting to believe the worst of him?

Pushing the wheelbarrow, she moved down the garden to the vacant plot she was preparing for her late crops, wrinkling her nose as she began to work fertiliser into the earth. It might be a good idea to have a bath before going into town this afternoon unless she wanted to be ostracised by the local shopkeepers, she thought ruefully, wiping the back of her hand across her perspiring forehead. She couldn't recall the fertiliser being quite so pungent before.

'Kat, Kat...'

Startled, she spun round, anxiety leaping into her eyes as she saw Jessica, clearly distressed, racing towards her.

'The woods...they're on fire...it's heading this way...'

Katherine began to run towards the house, fear gripping her as she saw dark columns rising into the sky. How could she have been so completely oblivious to what was happening around her, not smelt the acrid smoke settling in the air? That damn fertiliser! 'The fire brigade——'

'Daniel's already called them.' Jessica ran by her side. 'He noticed the fire first...tried to ring you... Oh, Kat, the thatch, look at the roof...'

'Come on, Katherine. It's in the hands of the professionals now. There's nothing we can do.'

Through a black blur of horror Katherine registered the deep voice by her side, was vaguely aware of the hand on her arm urging her towards a car.

'Everyone's trampling all over the garden. It's going to be such a mess.' She could hardly believe that it was her speaking. Why was she worrying about a few vegetables when her home was being destroyed in front of her? Her eyes were smarting from the smoke, her throat burning. At least everyone was safe...

'Thomas!' Violently she tore herself away from Daniel's grasp. 'He was in the linen cupboard upstairs...' Blindly she began to run towards the house, oblivious to the warning cries.

'Let me go...' She dodged the restraining arm, missed her footing and fell headlong on to the paved path. There was a sharp agonising pain and then she was floating in a grey, swirling mist.

From a great distance she heard voices but couldn't seem to understand what anyone was saying, couldn't seem to recognise any of the blurred faces that swam and disappeared in front of her eyes. There was something warm and sticky trickling down her cheek.

'It's all right. Just lie still. The ambulance is on its way.'

The deep, reassuring voice penetrated through the fog in her head.

'The twins...' She tried to sit up but firm, gentle hands held her immobile. Tim...oh, God...he wouldn't know about the fire yet...he couldn't just come home and find...someone had to tell him...Desperately she tried to claw her way back through the darkness that threatened to engulf her completely. 'James.' Her lifelong friend. He'd always been there when she needed him. He would take care of the twins. 'James...'

Katherine focused her eyes on the white-coated figure standing at the end of the bed. She thought it was the same doctor that had examined her earlier but couldn't be sure. Mild concussion. A gash on her temple. Bruises.

'Fortunately there doesn't seem to be any real damage, but we'll keep you in overnight just to be on the safe side.'

'Thank you, Doctor.' Heavens, it hurt to smile. 'But I really do feel fine.' Liar. 'If I could just have my clothes...'

'Come on, now, Miss Maitland, just get back in bed, please.' A nurse bustled over and smiled at her cheerfully. 'There's no point in getting worked up like this.'

'You don't understand...' She saw the determined expression on the uniformed woman's face and sighed defeatedly, scrambling back into bed. The minor rebellion seemed to have sapped all her strength. It was almost a relief to submit and sink back into the sheets, all too easy to close her eyes and stop thinking. She must have dozed off because when she opened her eyes again the ward was bathed in evening sunshine and a different nurse was looking down at her.

'You've some visitors to see you.' The nurse plumped up her pillows. 'Would you like to sit up?'

Obediently Katherine eased herself into a sitting position, looked expectantly towards the door and saw the twins sauntering casually into the ward.

'Hi, Kat. You look awful,' Tim greeted her cheerfully, and eyed her left temple with interest. 'Stitches?'

'Brought you some things.' Jessica placed a small bag in her locker and pulled up a chair. 'Soap, toothpaste, a towel.' She gazed around curiously and smiled at the woman in the bed opposite.

Katherine looked at her siblings in total disbelief. She'd expected them to be subdued, shocked, had envisaged white stunned faces. Instead they were acting as if nothing untoward had happened, as if having your home go up in flames was an everyday occurrence. Perhaps it was delayed shock, she thought with mounting anxiety, and then she understood. This show of nonchalance was all an act, put on for her benefit.

'So, what's been happening?' she asked lightly. If they wanted to underplay everything she would go along with it.

'Helped deliver a calf this morning,' Tim informed her laconically. 'Well, I just watched, actually, but it was terrific. It was a heifer and——'

'Tim,' Katherine cut in quietly. This was going a little too far!

'Fire's out.' Tim's voice thickened slightly. 'House is a bit of a mess, but probably worse than it looks.'

'Thomas?'

'No.'

Katherine picked at her sheet. 'I was stupid. I shouldn't have...' She swallowed. 'I'm sorry.' She'd let the twins down badly, landing herself in hospital at a time when they needed her.

'It's not your fault,' Jessica said brightly. 'And we're fine. We're staying with Mr and Mrs Sinclair tonight. They've been terrific. So's James. He picked up Tim from the vet's and then took us both shopping. He made us make a list of essentials. I bought you some underwear and another T-shirt.'

No more of Tim's discarded shirts and jumpers, Katherine thought, fighting the insane desire to burst into laughter. They were all going to need completely new wardrobes.

'We had to borrow some money from James . . .'

'That's OK. I'll sort that out with him.' The shopping expedition had also kept the twins occupied, probably helped to counteract the immediate shock by giving them something concrete to do. Silently she thanked James for his thoughtfulness. She'd known she could rely on him. Kind, safe, dependable James. He'd always been there at every crisis point in her life. How glad she was now that they had never become romantically involved. How much better to have him as a platonic friend for the rest of her life.

'James has contacted the insurance company, too,' Tim chipped in. 'He didn't want you to think he was interfering, but he thought it best to get things moving straight away.'

'Of course I don't think he's interfering,' Katherine said warmly. 'And you must thank him from me.'

'Thank him yourself,' Jessica grinned. 'He brought us over tonight and is waiting outside. Oh, and Mr and Mrs Sinclair send their love.' She rose to her feet. 'I'll go and tell James to come on in.'

Katherine watched her sister walk to the door. So the whole Sinclair family had rallied around with moral and practical help . . . with one notable exception. Daniel hadn't even bothered to send a message, let alone come and visit her in person. What had he done? Simply dismissed her from his mind the moment she'd been driven away in the ambulance? Automatically she smiled as she saw James approaching. It was odd, she reflected, that a few short weeks ago she'd have been in seventh heaven to see that expression of deep concern on his face. And now? Of course, she was pleased to see him, was glad that he still cared about her as a friend, but she just wished...hell, she wasn't sure what she wished. It was ridiculous, but when the twins had appeared she had for no logical reason just assumed that it was Daniel that had brought them to the hospital.

'Hey, stop worrying.' James kissed her lightly on the cheek. 'I think it's easy to say, but try and not think about it. It'll all work out.'

She nodded, feeling a total hypocrite.

'You know that Robyn and I will do anything at all we can to help.'

'Thanks.' Absently she observed that the twins had wandered to the far end of the ward and were engrossed in conversation with an elderly patient. 'Do you realise I haven't seen you since your wedding?' She turned her attention back to James. 'How was Crete?'

'Wonderful,' he smiled back. 'We've been meaning to ask you and the twins over for a meal one evening. I rather thought we'd bump into you at Daniel's. Has he been in tonight to see you?' he added casually.

'No.' Katherine's eyes dropped to her hands. 'Why? Did he say he was coming?' she murmured with equal casualness.

'Haven't seen him all day, actually. He phoned me at work this morning to tell me what happened, but no one's heard from him since. He's not at home...I know he was planning to go up to London this afternoon, so I suppose...' James broke off, frowning.

Katherine reached for the glass of water on her bedside table and took a sip. So Daniel hadn't even waited to find out how she was before tearing off to London. Even James seemed a little surprised at his total lack of concern.

'James...' She raised her head and looked directly into his face. This was hardly the most opportune time for the confession, but suddenly it became very important that she be completely honest with him, make certain that he didn't think that she'd been deliberately trying to avoid him over the past weeks. 'I used to think I was in love with you.' It was far easier to say, much less embarrassing than she would have believed possible. 'You knew that, didn't you?'

'Yes,' he agreed quietly. 'I knew you thought you were in love with me. I also realised that you weren't.'

With sudden panic Katherine searched his face. Did he have any inkling of what had lain behind her confused emotions?

'You had a tough time after your parents were killed,' James continued softly. 'You weren't able to go out socialising a great deal, meet other people as you would have done if you'd still been at college.' He shrugged. 'And I was always on the scene. You just mixed up friendship with something deeper because you were vulnerable, lonely...'

Katherine smiled. 'I suppose so.' Her eyes rested on him affectionately. If she ever did fall in love it would have to be with a man with James's qualities. Someone with his compassion and kindness, someone who would treat her as an equal, respect her as an individual, someone who would always be there when she needed him.

'I'm glad we had this conversation,' James said softly. 'It makes things much easier . . . with Robyn.'

'Yes.' Katherine nodded understandingly. She turned her head. 'Where did you get those, Tim?' she enquired drily as her brother reappeared, waving a box of chocolates at her.

'The lady in the end bed,' Jessica answered by his side. 'Her grandson bought them, but she can't eat the hard centres, so she gave them to us. Wasn't that sweet? Actually, I think she felt a bit sorry for us when I explained we normally lived off lettuce leaves.'

'And then when I told her we were homeless as well . . .' Tim's grin vanished and his face went white. 'That was stupid . . . I . . . Goodnight, Kat . . .' Abruptly he swung round and almost ran to the door, with Jessica tearing after him.

'I knew it was all bravado. I knew they'd crack up.' Katherine looked at James in desperation. 'Please go and make sure he's OK . . .' She swung her legs out of bed. 'I can't stay here tonight when the twins——'

'It's all right,' James murmured soothingly, pushing her back beneath the sheets. 'If Tim is going to have a good howl he won't want either you or me to witness it. And don't forget he's got Jessica.'

Katherine slumped back on her pillow and stared at the ceiling. The twins had each other. James had Robyn . . . and Daniel had Julia. Plus an estranged wife.

'Try and get some sleep.' James touched her cheek gently. 'I'll ring the hospital in the morning and find out what time you're being discharged.'

'Thanks . . . for everything.' Katherine's eyes followed his retreating figure across the ward and then flickered

to the wall clock. Another ten minutes before the bell
to announce the end of visiting hours. There was still
time... She squeezed her eyes shut. She just wanted to
fall asleep, sink into oblivion, forget everything.

'Appointment card for Out-patients. Now have you made
sure you've cleared your locker?'

Katherine nodded obediently, popping the proffered
card into her bag.

'Good.' The sudden warm smile transformed the severe
face. 'There's a young man pacing up and down in the
day-room, waiting for you. So I should hurry up and
collect him before he wears a hole in the carpet.'

'Thank you, Sister.' Katherine suppressed a grin and
sped away. She pushed open the door of the day-room,
momentarily blinded by the sunlight in her eyes.

'James, I'm sorry I kept you waiting...' She came to
an abrupt halt as she took a step into the room and
realised her error. The tall figure by the window swung
round to face her.

'Ready?' Without even a perfunctory greeting, Daniel
strode to the door.

'How are you? Feeling better? Those bruises must be
sore,' Katherine muttered under her breath as she hurried
after Daniel down the hospital corridors. He hadn't even
glanced at her! Presumably James had been too tied up
at work to collect her and delegated the chore to his ob-
viously unwilling brother. She flicked a quick glance at
his grim, uncompromising face. God, he was selfish, she
thought savagely, begrudging this relatively minor
demand on his time. Did it really hurt him to give her
a lift to his parents' home from the hospital?

'It's really sweet of you to come and collect me,' she murmured with a bright smile. 'I do hope it hasn't inconvenienced you too much.'

Daniel gave no indication that he had even heard her, but merely increased his pace.

'If you want to go on ahead, that's fine,' Katherine snapped, 'but I'm not in training for the London marathon.' With sudden clarity she remembered the warmth and concern James had shown her the evening before. It might have been too much to expect sympathy from Daniel, but he could at least treat her with civility instead of this thinly veiled hostility which she had done nothing to deserve. 'How the hell you and James could be brothers is beyond me!' She glared at the retreating figure as she emerged from the hospital into the sunlight, and then abruptly turned away and started walking in the opposite direction.

She was halfway down the high street when the red saloon drew up alongside her.

'Get in!' Daniel thundered, opening the passenger door.

'I'm getting a taxi...a bus...' she flung back from the pavement.

'Fine. Suit yourself.' Daniel slammed the door closed and, glancing over his shoulder, prepared to move back into the main stream of traffic.

He wouldn't...he couldn't... She wasn't carrying any money, didn't possess the fare for a bus, let alone a taxi, a fact that Daniel was probably perfectly aware of. She'd just been making a gesture, trying to prove a point...and he had called her bluff. Swiftly she wrenched hold of the door-handle and scrambled into the car. If he said one word... Head held high, she stared rigidly out of the window as Daniel drove out of the town on to a dual carriageway. She wasn't going to break the silence, was going ignore Daniel completely, regard him simply as a chauffeur.

'You would have driven off and left me stranded, wouldn't you?' Oh, she was so weak!

'Yes,' he agreed. 'You were behaving like a spoilt child, throwing a temper tantrum to get attention.'

Katherine's cheeks flamed with colour.

'Sorry, but I'm not wasting any sympathy on someone who ends up in hospital through their own reckless stupidity.' Without giving her any warning of his intention, he manoeuvred the car into a lay-by and slammed on the brakes. 'My God, how could you have been such a crazy little fool as to try and rush into a burning house? If you hadn't tripped over...' Hazel-gold eyes blazed into hers. 'You weren't just risking your own life...'

'Don't you think I know all that?' Katherine flared. She didn't need this. She was perfectly aware of how irresponsible she'd been, aware that she had caused a lot of people unnecessary trouble, had wasted public money needlessly.

'Don't you ever use your head, think before you act? No cat is worth the life of a human being. You're twenty-three years old, not some——'

'Animal-mad child of ten?' she ground through clenched teeth. Was that what this was really all about? Thirteen years ago she'd unwittingly risked her life to save a dog. Yesterday she'd been compelled to take the same risk for a cat—except this time the only person to suffer any injury had been herself. Was Daniel finally going to openly admit he blamed her—for something that had happened over a decade ago? A wave of disgust tore through her. How could anyone hold a grudge against the actions of a child for thirteen years? She was sick to death of feeling guilty. It wasn't as if she'd ruined his life—architecture might have been his second choice of career, but it had proved to be a highly successful one. Did it ever occur to him that he might have failed to make the grade in the highly competitive world of professional tennis anyway?

She held his gaze, chin raised challengingly. Hell, didn't he think she had enough on her plate right now without this? She frowned as she realised that the anger had ebbed from his face, the shutters clamping down over his eyes making them completely unreadable.

'Will there be a scar?' Unexpectedly, throwing her completely off balance, he gently swept the hair back from her forehead.

'I don't know...I never thought to ask.' She flicked him a wary, puzzled glance as he started the ignition and then settled back in her seat.

If she was predictable then Daniel was the complete reverse. These swift mood changes of his that seemed so prevalent of late never failed to take her by surprise. He never used to be so mercurial, she mused with dark, thoughtful eyes. She'd always known exactly what to expect from him. But now when she encountered him she was never sure if she was going to be greeted by a man with a familiar lazy, mocking smile or a grim-faced stranger. Today was a classic example. His anger earlier on had almost been a tangible physical force, and now, without any warning, it had evaporated—and she had done nothing to either cause it or pacify it. She wouldn't mind so much if he simply lost his temper and started shouting. But he never lost control of himself. His voice didn't rise the way hers did when she was angry, but deepened, became quieter, which was somehow far more alarming.

'This isn't the way to your mother's.' She frowned, suddenly aware of her surroundings.

'No.' Daniel paused at the crossroads and turned right into the familiar lane. 'I thought you might like to have a look at the house,' he said quietly.

Katherine swallowed. Time to face reality. 'The twins didn't tell me much. Is..., is it repairable or will it have to be demolished?'

'These old houses were built to last.' He gave her a sideways smile. 'I don't think you'll be able to salvage much from inside, but the basic structure appears to be pretty sound.' He rounded a bend and Katherine caught her first glimpse of the blackened shell that had once been her home.

As he drew to a halt she climbed from the car and just stared, the full horror of what had happened finally seeming to hit her. Her home for twenty-three years. All those memories. Furniture, clothes...they could all be replaced. But those other far more precious things were gone forever.

'My mother still has some photographs of your parents. I'm sure she'll be only too glad to give them to you.'

The gentleness in Daniel's voice, his perceptiveness, made her eyes mist over. 'Thank you.'

'I'll wait for you by the car.'

She nodded silently, grateful that he seemed to understand that she needed some time on her own. Slowly she walked around the house, exploring it from all angles, and then wandered down the garden. It looked as if a herd of elephants had trampled over it, she thought sadly. Those vegetables remaining were scorched, covered in a film of ash. At least the greenhouse was still intact, and the wooden shed where she kept her tools seemed also to have escaped by some miracle.

She frowned. Someone had fastened a new padlock to the shed door, which she'd left unlocked yesterday with the key still hanging on a hook in the kitchen. Her eyes softened, deeply moved by the thoughtful action. James? In the unlikely event that her gardening equipment had been stolen, it would have been covered by her insurance. But that wasn't the point. She would have hated to lose any of her tools... they'd become curiously personal to her over the years.

She walked across to the greenhouse and entered it. Instinctively she touched the soil at the base of the tomato plants. Damp. Whoever had fixed the padlock must have tended to her greenhouse crops as well. That someone had even remembered, cared enough... A lump formed in her throat and she dashed a hand across her eyes.

Slowly she retraced her steps back towards the car, pausing to touch the trunk of the huge indomitable oak tree. It had survived the storms and hurricane-force winds of the past few years, and now had escaped the fire. Wounded with singed leaves and scorched branches, but still alive. She looked upwards, knowing it was ridiculous, that there was no hope, but...

Her disbelieving eyes caught the whisk of ginger fur and, moving too late, she yelped as sharp claws dug into her shoulder.

'Get off, you monster!'

The cat leapt down and darted away.

'Are you all right?' Daniel reached her side. 'Not your average cuddly moggy, is he?'

'More like Jekyll and Hyde.' She swallowed hard. 'I suppose it would be best to leave him here for now and come over and feed him every day. I'd never manage to catch him anyway.' She was rambling but couldn't seem to stop. 'Oh, Thomas... I really thought he'd been in the house... that...' The tears she'd held back for so long started to pour down her cheeks. Hardly aware of what she was doing, she launched herself against Daniel and, twining her arms around his neck, buried her head in his shoulder. She just wanted to be held, craved the warmth and strength of another human being.

She felt him stir against her and, stiffening with embarrassment, realised that he was pushing her away, disentangling her arms from his neck.

'Shall we go?' Not waiting for a response, he walked over to the car and held the passenger door open for her.

'Thank you.' She couldn't look at him, couldn't remember when she'd last felt so awkward or self-conscious. She'd only wanted a hug, for heaven's sake! Her mouth tightened, her eyes darkening with resentment, hating him for making her feel such a fool. Daniel was quite willing to touch her, to kiss her when it amused him to do so, but when she'd just wanted to be held, to be comforted, he'd simply pushed her away. He was devoid of all human warmth and compassion. How could he sit there beside her, looking so unconcerned, whistling softly under his breath as he steered the powerful car along the narrow, winding lane?

'Incidentally, I've contacted McCauley's. One of the chaps came over yesterday evening to have a quick look round and is coming back tomorrow afternoon to work out a rough estimate.'

Lost in thought, it took Katherine a few seconds to absorb Daniel's casually tossed words.

'You've been in touch with a builder? Asked them for an estimate on *my* house...without consulting me first?'

'It's only an estimate,' Daniel murmured calmly, 'but, if you want my advice, you'll accept it. You don't want to let some cowboy outfit loose on the house. McCauley's are a very reputable firm and specialise in renovating old buildings.'

'I don't want your advice! I'm quite capable of making my own decisions without any help from you.' Would he have been quite so interested if she'd lived in a modern bungalow? It was the actual building he was concerned about, not the fact that it happened to be her home. 'You had absolutely no right to interfere in my business!'

She could have bitten off her tongue the moment she'd spoken as realisation dawned on her. Daniel had been at the house yesterday evening...it was he who had padlocked the shed and watered the plants. Hell! Perhaps he'd genuinely been trying to help her by arranging for a builder to come over and inspect what remained of the house. If nothing else, he had saved her the anxiety of waiting to discover whether the house could be saved. She'd hadn't objected in the slightest on learning that James had contacted the insurance company without her knowledge, and yet when Daniel had acted comparably she'd turned on him like a virago. And she didn't need to be a psychologist to work out why. She'd lashed out at him because she'd been angry, still smarting from the way he'd rebuffed her earlier. She would never understand Daniel. He'd been considerate enough to water her plants, and yet when she'd reached out to him for human comfort he'd shown as much warmth as a block of ice. She was doubtlessly blowing the whole incident out of all proportion, being super-sensitive, but his cold-blooded rejection had damn well hurt. It still hurt. And that's what really rankled, the disturbing realisation that Daniel had the power to cause her that degree of pain.

Unhappily she looked at him from under her lashes. His face was devoid of all expression, but she could see a muscle flickering in the lean jaw. The peacemaker inside her badly wanted to apologise, try and make amends, break the unbearable, strained silence, but another part of her stubbornly refused to let the words form on her lips. With dark, clouded eyes she gazed out of the window but had no real recollection of the short journey to the Sinclair family home.

As Daniel swung into the gravel drive of the pleasant red-bricked house she reached into the back seat to collect her small bag. The car came to a halt, but Daniel kept the engine running.

'Aren't you coming in to see your mother?' Katherine opened the door.

'No.'

She scrambled out of the car and then paused irres-olutely, gazing at the harsh, forbidding profile through the open window. 'Daniel . . . I'm . . .' Couldn't he even look at her when she was speaking? 'Thanks for the lift,' she muttered finally.

Hands sunk in the pockets of her jeans, she watched the red saloon disappear down the drive and walked de-jectedly around the side of the house.

CHAPTER SEVEN

CHEWING the top of her pen, Katherine scanned the classified section in the local evening paper and then with a sigh tossed the paper on to the wicker chair next to her. Trying to find rented accommodation for herself and the twins was proving to be as great a problem as she'd anticipated.

'Hopeless,' she informed the black Labrador dog sprawled by her feet on the patio. 'No problem if I were a third person. But nobody seems to want three persons.'

The Labrador raised its head, licked her hand sympathetically and then hopefully nosed the rubber ball planted between its front paws. Obligingly Katherine threw the ball down the garden and watched the dog tear after it, tail wagging furiously.

The last few days had passed in a whirl of activity, completing endless paperwork for the insurance company, contacting the bank, cancelling the orders from the shops to whom she sold her produce, shopping for clothes and other essentials. She'd quickly discovered, too, that it was the loss of the minor little items that was the most irritating. Like yesterday, when Tim had lost a button off his shirt, and she'd instinctively started to look for the family button box.

She'd found it difficult to relax, virtually impossible to stop her mind from ticking over, was constantly remembering something else she had failed to do—all of which seemed to entail yet more form-filling. She must advise the Post Office of her temporary change of address . . . apply for a new driving licence . . . MOT and insurance documentation for the van . . . passport. She was sleeping badly, waking up in the middle of the night, worrying about something completely trivial. Last night she'd lain tossing and turning in bed because she hadn't as yet officially cancelled the milk and newspaper deliveries.

'I have a sneaking suspicion that this wasn't such a good idea,' she murmured as the Labrador retrieved the ball, crouched by her side and gazed up at her with expectant brown eyes. 'This is the last time? OK? Oh, well, have it your own way,' she added as the dog bounded to its paws and raced away around the side of the house.

Shivering slightly, she reached for the new cream sweater draped over the back of her chair, tugged it over her head and shook the thick mane of fair hair back over her shoulder. The dying sun's rays were turning the western sky blood-red; the still air was filled with the fragrance of night-scented stock and roses. Stretching her arms above her head, Katherine breathed in the delicate perfume and felt the tension beginning to ease from her body.

She heard the crunch of footsteps on gravel and the brief moment of tranquillity evaporated as she saw Daniel, dressed with unusual formality in a grey suit, turning the corner of the house, the black dog close on his heels.

Picking up the newspaper, he dropped his long, lean frame into the chair by her side and surveyed the livid bruises on her cheek. 'Purple always was your colour.'

'Pity. Because I think I'm just about to enter my yellow phase.' Daniel seemed to have completely forgotten the constraint under which they'd last parted, but she was not deceived by his casual air of good humour, was only too aware of how quickly that could change.

'Stitches are healing well.'

'Thank you, Dr Sinclair.' She was beginning to feel a little self-conscious under his continuing scrutiny. 'Your parents are having dinner with some friends. I'm not sure when they'll be back.' Presumably they were the reason for his unexpected visit.

'And the twins?'

'Tim's at the cricket club, and Jesse has gone to the cinema with Andy.' She saw Daniel raise a dark eyebrow. 'He's a nice boy,' she said a little defensively. And she was finally learning to accept that the twins were growing up.

'Actually, it was you I came to see anyway.' Daniel leaned back in his chair, loosened his tie, and stretched out his legs in front of him.

Katherine concealed her surprise and looked at him enquiringly. He looked tired, she observed. Overwork or overplay? The twins had resumed their holiday jobs the day after her release from hospital and she'd learned via Jessica of Daniel's frequent trips to London. Judging by his formal attire, he'd been up there today. Business or pleasure? she wondered caustically.

'Jesse told me you're looking for rented accommodation?'

'Mmm.' Her sister had never been renowned for her discretion. 'Your parents have been absolutely wonderful but I can't expect them to put us up indefinitely. And it could be months until we can go home. McCauley's can't even give me a start date yet, so heaven knows when they'll actually complete the work.'

'So you decided to accept the McCauley's estimate?'

She glanced at him quickly, suspicious of the curious
note in his voice, but could learn nothing from the bland
expression on his face.

'Mmm. Assuming it's okayed by the insurance
company, but the agent who brought round the claims
forms didn't think there would be any problems.' She
paused, leaning out of her chair to fondle the Labrador's
silky black ears. 'I'm sorry I bit your head off the other
day,' she muttered finally, and saw him shrug dismissively. He'd probably forgotten her outburst until she'd
reminded him, had simply erased it from his mind as
unimportant. Whereas she seemed to have total recall
where Daniel was concerned, she realised with a sense
of shock, could virtually recount their every conversation word for word, could visualise in her mind with
startling ease the expressions that had crossed his face.

'Any luck so far?'

Her mind went a complete blank for a second and
then, pulling herself together hurriedly, she shook her
head. 'I went to see one cottage yesterday afternoon that
sounded promising, but for some reason the owner
seemed horrified at the idea of sixteen-year-old twins.'
Why did she find the dark shadow around Daniel's jaw
and chin so fascinating? Did he use an electric shaver
or a more traditional razor? She hoped it was the latter,
could almost smell the tang of male shaving foam. Hell,
what had she been talking about...? She forced a grin
to her lips, hoping it looked more natural and spontaneous than it felt. 'He kept mumbling that he had no
objections to pets or children...but teenagers! Of course,
they didn't mean to be so clumsy, noisy or irresponsible,
and of course they weren't all delinquents but...' She
could laugh about it now but it hadn't been funny at the
time, merely frustrating and disappointing. Surely Daniel

wasn't really interested in all this anyway? She raised her eyes and looked at him levelly. 'What did you want to see me about?' she asked bluntly.

'I've a business proposition to put to you.' He folded his arms idly behind his head, his shirt tautening across the deep, powerful chest. 'Of course, you may not be interested.' He smiled and lapsed into an infuriating silence.

Katherine waited a few seconds and gave in. 'All right, I've taken the bait. Go ahead.'

'I need a gardener, you need a roof over your head. Solution?'

'In return for mowing your lawn or what's left of it, I get to camp out in the potting shed?'

'If you have a wild, burning desire to take up residence in my potting shed I wouldn't dream of standing in your way. But the twins might prefer to stay in the house.'

Katherine searched his face. 'You're serious, aren't you?' Why exactly was he offering her this way out of her present difficulty? There were plenty of retired or semi-retired men in the area who would be more than willing to work on his garden, glad of some extra income.

A small smile tugged at the corner of Daniel's mouth as he saw the suspicion in her eyes. 'No catches. No ulterior motive. A simple business arrangement. So what do you say?'

'Head gardener at Norrington Hall. Should look impressive on my CV.' She was playing for time, refused to be rushed into making a snap decision. In theory it seemed an ideal solution to her problem. The twins would love living at Norrington Hall. Thomas, according to Jessica, was now practically a permanent resident anyway. She would be near enough to work on her own garden, tend to the limited crops that remained. There was just one problem . . . Daniel.

'Of course, if you think that the wilderness I fondly refer to as my garden is going to be a little too much for you to tackle . . .' Daniel raised his hands in front of him in a mocking gesture of defeat.

Katherine ignored him. She wasn't going to bite. Slowly, eyes pensive, she rose to her feet and meandered down the garden. Living under the same roof as Daniel. Seeing him every day. First thing in the morning. Last thing at night. Sharing his home. Her stomach turned a somersault.

'You and the twins would be virtually self-contained.' She'd felt his presence behind her even before he'd spoken. 'We probably wouldn't see each other for days on end.'

'You mean I wouldn't have to report to your study each morning for my day's orders, touching my forelock?' she enquired drily, turning to face him. Had he guessed her thoughts yet again, or was he simply warning her that he wouldn't accept any intrusion into his privacy, laying down some form of ground rules?

'You can have a completely free hand with the garden. Do whatever you like,' he said easily. 'So you'll accept my offer?'

'Yes,' she agreed quietly.

'Good.' Before she had time to register what was happening he tilted his head and dropped a quick kiss on her mouth. 'Bargain sealed. Move in whenever suits you. Tomorrow if you like.' Turning away, he strode back towards the house, raising his hand in a farewell salute as he vanished around the corner.

Don't over-react, Katherine told herself firmly. It had been nothing more than a brief, casual peck, for goodness' sake. Not worth a second thought. Packing, she thought resolutely. That's what she ought to start thinking about, gathering up all the new possessions she and the twins had acquired over the last few days. Resolutely she headed for the house.

Katherine closed her book and uncurled herself from the armchair. 'Supper, anyone?' she enquired to the room at large, and received three incoherent grunts in reply.

Tim and Jessica were sprawled on the carpet by the fireplace; Daniel was stretched out on the brocade-covered chesterfield. Katherine's mouth curved in a smile as her eyes moved from the two fair heads to the russet one, studying the absorbed expression on each of the three faces bent over the books in their hands. Why was reading silently together so much more companionable an activity than watching television?

Humming softly under her breath, she walked through the hall to the kitchen and switched on the kettle. She set four cups and saucers on a tray and opened a cupboard door, retrieving the packet of cheese crackers to which Daniel was currently addicted. Mustn't forget to remind Ellen to add them to the weekly shopping list, she mused, and then pulled herself up abruptly. It wasn't her place to remind Daniel's housekeeper about anything. She was a guest in this house, that was all. No, not a guest, she amended quickly, an employee, and a temporary one at that. A fact, she realised with a jolt, that was becoming increasingly easy to forget.

She walked over to the window and watched the raindrops trickle down the panes of glass. The weather had finally broken this afternoon, had forced her indoors for the first time since her arrival. Three weeks ago! It was hard to believe that she and the twins had been here for that length of time. The days had passed so easily, one uncomplicated day drifting into the next. The luxury of coming down each morning to find Ellen waiting to serve breakfast. The mornings spent in the garden. Lunch a sandwich shared with Jessica and Ellen in the kitchen. Sometimes they were joined by Daniel, but more often than not he remained working in his study.

'Don't ever disturb Daniel when he's in his study,' both Jessica and the grey-haired widowed housekeeper had warned her, following it up with graphic descriptions of the fate that might befall her if she possessed the temerity to do so.

'He always comes out when he gets hungry enough,' Ellen had added peacefully.

Like a lion emerging from his lair, Katherine had mused silently.

If her days were structured, governed by the hours of daylight and mealtimes, Daniel's followed no such orthodox pattern. She'd seen little of him during her first week. He'd disappeared into his study for hours on end, been driven out finally either by hunger pangs or a seemingly frenetic desire for physical activity. Pounding relentlessly up and down the swimming pool. Striding around the grounds, hands sunk into the pockets of his jeans, eyes dark with concentration. Riding if it wasn't too hot. Energy spent, he'd returned to his study, working late into the night. Sometimes, Katherine suspected, all night.

She'd always supposed that Daniel's meteoric rise to success had been achieved through luck as much as anything else. Of course, he presumably had some talent, she'd admitted grudgingly. But now for the first time it occurred to her that sheer hard work and determination might have played some part in that success. She'd always been completely taken in by that casual air of indolence, she realised, had never even suspected that he possessed these workaholic tendencies.

'Doesn't it irritate you, never knowing if Daniel is going to turn up for meals you've cooked?' Katherine asked Ellen curiously one evening after Daniel had failed yet again to make an appearance at the dinner table. It would drive a lot of women to distraction, she thought privately.

'It did at first,' the older women admitted. 'But I've got used to him now. That's why I usually make a casserole that he can heat up when ever he's ready, or just leave a salad.' Ellen smiled. 'I wouldn't have him any different.'

'Really?' Katherine murmured politely. She could think of one or two improvements.

It was at the beginning of her second week that Katherine, on her return from dropping Tim off at the bus-stop, discovered Daniel still lingering at the breakfast table with Jessica. Normally he'd retreated to his study by now, she thought with surprise.

'Ellen,' he glanced up as the housekeeper began to clear away the used dishes, 'sandwiches and a couple of flasks, please.'

Puzzled, Katherine witnessed the expressions of pleasurable anticipation that instantly crossed the housekeeper's and her sister's faces. Pouring a cup of tea, she took a long sip, and surveyed Daniel over the rim of her cup with growing suspicion.

He smiled back at her blandly. 'We're going on picnic.'

'As in the royal we?'

'We as in Ellen, Jessica, Katherine...'

'Ah, a staff outing? Sorry, I don't think I've been here long enough to qualify.'

'I'll waive the rules. Just this once,' he murmured obligingly.

'Don't bother on my account.'

'As you wish.' Newspaper in hand, he rose to his feet and departed from the room.

'Oh, Kat, why don't you come with us?' Jessica turned on her immediately. 'It's great fun. We never know where we're going until we get there. Last time we went to Winchester because Daniel wanted to take some photographs of the cathedral, and then we had a picnic in the New Forest on the way home.'

'You mean you and Ellen often go out for the day with Daniel?'

'Not always for the day. Sometimes just the afternoon, maybe just for a few hours.' Jessica's face lit up with enthusiasm. 'We've visited Wilton House, Kingston Lacy, Breamore House——'

'But you hate looking around old houses!' Katherine interjected, recalling all too vividly her sister's groans of protest when she'd suggested similar expeditions.

'It's more interesting with Daniel somehow.' She paused. 'I never mentioned these trips before because you used to get so moody if I talked about Daniel.'

'I think you must have imagined that,' Katherine said lightly. 'Now, I suppose you'd better go and get ready.'

'Mmm. I'll have to see to the horses first. Oh, Kat, do change your mind and come.'

'No.' She wasn't going to jump every time Daniel clicked his fingers, even if Jessica and Ellen were prepared to do so. Just because he felt like a day out and wanted company! Huh! She frowned with growing mystification. A schoolgirl and an elderly widow didn't seem the most obvious choice of companions for Daniel. Perhaps he simply wanted an audience to whom he could air his knowledge and Jessica and Ellen just happened to be on hand.

'You know why he invites us to go with him, don't you?' Jessica's hushed voice broke through her thoughts. 'For Ellen. Only if he includes me in the outings it doesn't look too obvious that he feels sorry for her. Her husband only died three months ago, you know, just after they moved down from London to retire. She doesn't know many people around here yet; hasn't any family.'

'I didn't realise,' Katherine said quietly, shame biting into her at the realisation that on this occasion it was Jessica who had shown the greater maturity. Why did she so consistently refuse to acknowledge Daniel's qualities, even when they were staring her in the face? Hadn't she already noticed that, while he might become so engrossed in his work that he didn't even remember to eat, he'd never once forgotten to escort Ellen home each evening to her cottage?

'It's only a mile down the lane,' Ellen had confided to her. 'But Daniel always insists on making sure I'm home safely. When he's away for the day he even arranges for a taxi to pick me up.'

Considerate. Kind. Daniel had always been those things; she'd just stubbornly and perversely persisted in closing her mind to them. What else had it been but an act of kindness, inviting herself and the twins to share his home? Offering her the post of gardener had simply been a way of making it easier for her to accept the invitation without having to feel completely beholden to him.

Oh, goodness, the kitchen was full of steam, the kettle nearly dry. Shaking herself mentally, Katherine refilled the kettle. This tendency to drift off into a daydream was becoming more and more prevalent of late. Even more troubling was the knowledge that it was almost invariably Daniel who preoccupied her thoughts. Familiarity was supposed to breed contempt, wasn't it? she thought wryly. But the reverse seemed to be happening in her case. Daniel had changed, she mused. No. It was she who'd changed over the last few weeks. She'd become less intransigent, less judgemental, had stopped fighting Daniel mentally all the time. Face it: she'd grown to like him. Liked the sound of his deep voice, liked the way his eyes laughed when something amused him, liked watching the different expressions move across his face when he thought he was unobserved. Liked the way he sometimes sneaked down to the kitchen in the middle of the night and helped himself to a huge chunk of Ellen's home-made fruit cake. She grinned. She'd caught him out one night when, woken up by thirst, she'd come downstairs for a glass of water. He'd looked like a guilty schoolboy for a second as she'd opened the kitchen door, she remembered, her eyes softening. Sat there in his robe, hair tousled, surrounded by cake crumbs.

'Don't grass on me to Ellen,' he'd grinned at her. 'Or I'll get a lecture on eating regular meals.' He'd indicated the cake tin. 'Like some?'

Katherine smiled. They'd sat there eating fruit cake and talking until the early hours. Had laughed a lot. Perhaps because she'd still been half asleep, or because the lateness of the hour had made everything unreal, she'd felt no constraint in his presence, had completely forgotten she was only clad, like him, in a dressing-gown. It had seemed the most natural thing in the world, too, when they'd finally parted on the top of the stairs, that

Daniel should press a warm kiss on her mouth. Equally natural that she should return it.

'Nice,' he'd murmured softly, smiling down into her face. 'Want to come and tuck me up?'

She'd known he was only teasing, but her heart had skipped a beat, warmth stealing through her body.

'I'm a gardener, not a nanny,' she'd returned lightly, determined that he shouldn't know just how rattled she was, and then she'd spoilt the whole effect by scuttling down the landing to her room like a startled rabbit.

When Ellen had announced during breakfast the following morning that Thomas was failing in his feline duties, as some human-sized mice had been at the fruit cake during the night, she'd been unable to return Daniel's conspiratorial grin, had refused to even look at him, kept her eyes fixed steadily on her cereal bowl. She'd felt embarrassed, uncertain, insecure, and wasn't even a hundred per cent sure why.

OK, so she liked Daniel, Katherine shrugged, picking up the tray of cups. It was no big deal. The twins liked him, Ellen liked him . . . even Thomas liked him. Motion carried. Daniel Sinclair is likeable. End of story.

Nudging the kitchen door open with her shoulder, she carried the tray back into the the drawing-room and placed it on a low table within everyone's reach.

'Help yourselves,' she murmured, picking up her own cup and settling back into an armchair. Someone had pulled the rich brown velvet drapes across the windows and switched on the lamps, bathing the room in soft lighting.

'Thanks,' Daniel smiled at her from over the top of his book and absently reached out for a biscuit.

Bookcases lined the wall at the far end of the room and Katherine had spent one contented evening perusing their contents. Daniel appeared to have a wide catholic taste in literature, and she'd discovered many of her personal favourites among his collection, including some much-loved children's classics. She'd been amused and touched to see the well-thumbed, worn editions and wondered if Daniel, like herself, could never bring himself to discard a book.

'Jesse, give Tim a nudge,' Katherine said softly, observing her brother's closed eyes and slowly drooping head.

Roused by his twin's unsympathetic poke in the ribs, Tim blinked dazedly for a second, picked up a cup, swallowed the contents in one long gulp and jumped to his feet.

'Going to bed. See you in the morning.'

'Think I'll go too.' Unsuccessfully concealing a yawn, Jessica followed her twin across the room. 'Night.'

As soon as the door closed behind them Katherine rose to her feet, collected the dirty crockery and picked up the tray.

'Don't go yet. Stay and talk to me for a while.'

She paused halfway across the room as she heard the soft, persuasive voice behind her, and, turning round, surveyed Daniel a little uncertainly.

'Come and sit down.' He swung his legs to the floor and patted the space on the sofa beside him. 'I've hardly seen you at all this week,' he murmured, smiling up into her eyes.

'You've been in your study most evenings,' she said lightly, trying to suppress the bubble of warmth building up inside her. With a casualness she was far from feeling she placed the tray back on the coffee-table and, hesitating only momentarily, joined him on the sofa.

'And you've been working outside until it's dark.' He turned to face her, leaning back against the arm-rest. 'So tell me what you've been doing. How are you getting on with the rose garden?'

The warm bubble disintegrated. Was that what he wanted, a progress report? Briskly, determined to ignore the sudden sense of deflation, she explained that, having dug up some of the old roses, she was currently exchanging the soil in the rose bed for fresh soil from another part of the garden. 'It's not a good idea to plant new roses where old ones have been,' she elucidated, seeing his frown. 'The soil's probably become ''rose sick'', although other plants will be quite happy in it.'

'So, instead of moving the rose garden to a different spot, you're changing the soil over?' Seeing her nod, he grinned. 'Ah, so that's why you've been trundling up and down with the wheelbarrow full of earth.'

She jolted, disconcerted to realise that he must have been watching her without her knowledge. Trundling? Huh! She most certainly did not trundle! 'I've ordered some new roses from the nursery.' He'd told her to spend whatever she felt necessary on the garden, so she had taken him at his word. 'They'll be ready to plant late autumn.' Late autumn. It was highly unlikely that she would still be here then. McCauley's had started on the house at the beginning of the week and already seemed to have accomplished a great deal. She frowned. Daniel would probably have a new gardener by the autumn. Odd how much she resented the idea of some unknown person planting the roses she had selected with such painstaking care. She was beginning to think of the garden as hers, she thought with a rush of unease, subconsciously making long-term plans for improvements which she would never get a chance to implement.

'You've certainly made a lot of headway already,' Daniel commented, 'but I don't expect you to work twenty-four hours a day, seven days a week.' He paused reflectively. 'Make it twenty-three hours...hmm? And Sunday afternoons off?' His words were flippant, but there was an underlying seriousness in his voice. 'I'm not planning to open the garden to the public.'

She had been putting in long hours in the garden but it had been through choice, not because she felt any pressure to do so. Besides, relieved of all the usual household chores by Ellen and a daily cleaning woman, she had nothing else to occupy her time, and she couldn't simply sit around all day doing nothing.

'When you're not working here you're working on your own garden,' Daniel continued quietly. 'Except for your trip to the hospital to have your stitches out, you've hardly been out since you arrived.'

She shrugged, slightly puzzled by his concern. And he was hardly in a position to talk, anyway, considering that, except for his trip with Ellen and Jessica, he'd not left the grounds either. Much to her surprise, his social life had been as non-existent as her own over the past few weeks.

'Take a day off.'

'Maybe I will,' she murmured evasively. She had no particular desire to go anywhere, she suddenly realised, and the thought of simply going out and aimlessly filling in a day for the sheer sake of it seemed pointless. Maybe she was turning into a recluse as well as a compulsive gardener, she thought with an inward smile. Odd. But even during the evenings when Ellen had gone home, the twins were out and Daniel was confined to his study, she never felt lonely. That restlessness she'd experienced before the fire seemed to have dissipated completely. Her eyebrows knitted together. She had lost all her possessions, nearly lost her home, and yet she felt happier than she had for months. She ought to be worrying about a completion date on the house, fretting about having to build up her business virtually from scratch again, and yet she barely even thought about either.

'Thursday.'

'Sorry?' She collected her thoughts quickly.

'Take Thursday off.'

She wrinkled her nose. 'I really don't want...' Her voice trailed off as he reached out and picked up her hand. Turning it over, he examined her palm.

'Been wearing your gloves. Good,' he murmured.

'I never did thank you,' she said lightly. The morning after her arrival she'd come down to breakfast and found a parcel containing three pairs of gardening gloves waiting for her. Her heart skipped an uncomfortable beat as Daniel's fingers began to trace the line of a recent scratch on her bare arm.

'Tetanus jabs up to date?'

'Of course.' Her voice wasn't quite steady, her eyes following the long fingers as they moved in slow, languorous circles over the sensitive skin on her forearm. He was only touching her arm, for goodness' sake— yet the hypnotic warmth he was creating was seeping through her entire being. Soothing. Relaxing. Soporific. His hand trailed up her arm and closed around her shoulder, gently but firmly kneading the tired muscles at the base of her neck. It suddenly seemed the most natural thing in the world to let her head fall against his chest.

'Shaftesbury.'

'Mmm?' Lean, sensitive fingers were stroking the hair back from her face, sending little waves of delight tingling down her spine.

'I thought we might go there on Thursday.'

She tried to break her way back through the bubble of warm, sensuous pleasure. 'We, as in...'

'We, as in you and I,' he murmured softly. 'If I can manage to tear you away from the garden.'

She smiled absently. It wasn't the garden that had bound her to Norrington Hall for the last three weeks. It had been Daniel. That she might hardly see him some days hadn't seemed to matter. She'd felt a strange, peaceful contentment just knowing that he was close by.

She felt his mouth brush against her temple and stirred, tilting her face upwards. He was looking down at her through dark, half-closed eyes, his mouth a few inches above hers. Dreamily she stretched up a hand, exploring the rugged planes of his face with gentle, caressing fingers. She traced the tenacious line of his jaw and touched the firm, straight mouth, a *frisson* of pleasurable anticipation shivering through her. That longing to feel his mouth against hers was a physical pain, growing more and more intense as he prolonged the agony of waiting.

'Kiss me. Please.' A voice she hardly recognised as her own muttered with imploring need.

'No.'

The warmth ebbed from her body, her face stiffening into a mask of shocked, humiliating pain.

'If I start kissing you, touching you, it's not going to stop there.' Daniel's voice was so low that it was barely audible. 'You're going to end up in my bed.'

My God, the arrogant, conceited... Did he seriously believe that after one kiss she'd be prepared to leap into bed with him? She raised her eyes to his face and as she witnessed the lines of strain etched around his mouth, saw the naked desire in his eyes, the words of outrage died on her lips. Disbelief, bewilderment gave way to incredulity. It was his own self-control that he doubted, not hers.

'Daniel...' she began hesitantly, but the remainder of her words choked in her throat as, giving her no warning, Daniel bent his head and kissed her with a fierce hunger that left her trembling and shaken.

'Now do you believe me?' he demanded huskily. Rising to his feet abruptly, he moved with uncharacteristic jerky movements across the room and, without looking round, closed the door behind him.

Katherine sat motionless on the sofa, staring straight ahead with dazed eyes. If she rushed after Daniel right now... oh, God, the temptation to throw all caution to the winds, to completely abandon sanity and reason. Slowly she stood up and walked out of the room into the deserted hall and up the stairs.

Deliberately avoiding even glancing at Daniel's door, she made her way along the length of the landing to her own bedroom. She switched on the light and sat down in the middle of the bed, hugging her knees to her chest. Daniel wasn't just physically attracted to her, bombshell though that was. He must care about her too, mustn't he? Just a weeny bit. Wasn't his restraint tonight indicative of that? He could have made love to her—of that she had no doubt. If he'd been determined to seduce her she would have been powerless to resist, wouldn't have wanted to, she admitted candidly. And she was equally sure that in the cold light of day she would have bitterly regretted it. But Daniel had taken charge of the situation long before it reached the danger point. Surely that showed he had some feelings for her, that he was at least sufficiently concerned about her not to want to hurt her?

Scrambling off the bed, she padded across the room to the *en suite* bathroom. That was one particular luxury she was going to certainly miss when she returned home. The bathroom or Daniel? Which was she going to miss most? she mused flippantly, and her heart constricted painfully. Not funny at all.

She stripped off her clothes and stepped under the shower. So what the hell happened now? Did she and Daniel simply greet each other in the morning as if nothing had happened? She frowned. But then nothing had happened, had it? Despite the warmth of the water, she felt a cold chill move up her spine. Had it actually been her, Katherine Maitland, whom Daniel had wanted to share his bed with tonight? Or simply that he had needed a woman? How long was it since he'd last seen Julia? The bar of soap slipped from her hand. She knew exactly how she would have felt if she'd woken up in Daniel's bed tomorrow morning. Sick to the stomach. Scowling, she switched off the shower and began to rub herself ferociously with a towel.

She tugged her cotton nightdress over her head, picked up her toothbrush and stared at it blankly. Daniel had asked her to go to Shaftesbury with him on Thursday. Abruptly her mood see-sawed upwards, a small fluttering happiness bursting over her. The fact that he wanted to spend a day in her company surely proved something, hmm? Of course, he might have changed his mind by the morning... Oh, heck, this compulsion to keep analysing everything Daniel said or did was futile and had to stop. She inevitably reached the wrong conclusion anyway. She squeezed toothpaste on to her brush and pulled a face as she glimpsed herself in the mirror above the basin. How could she look so serene, so composed and be such a gibbering wreck inside?

Katherine stopped outside the door of the breakfast-room and took a deep breath. Just act naturally, as if nothing has happened, she instructed herself. Schooling her features into a cheerful smile, she pushed open the door. 'Good morning. Another heavenly day.' Humming tunelessly, she pulled back her chair and sat down.

Tim and Jessica glanced up from their cereal bowls. 'All right, Kat?'

'Of course,' she said brightly. Where was Daniel? Had he already had breakfast? 'Why?'

Tim shrugged. 'You're just a bit…odd. Normally you don't even grunt until you've had a cup of tea. And you're wearing a skirt.'

'And it looks as if it's going to rain again any minute,' Jessica stated flatly, eyeing her sister curiously. 'You've put some lipstick on.'

Katherine glanced out of the window, the heavy grey clouds confirming Jessica's prognosis. 'Well, we could certainly do with some more rain,' she beamed, and saw the twins exchange glances before resuming their breakfast. So much for acting naturally! Apparently, grumpy and scruffy were her norms in the morning. Her eyes darted to the door as it opened, and then she relaxed.

'Morning, Ellen.'

'Scrambled eggs?' the housekeeper enquired, placing a pot of tea on the table.

'Just toast, please.' She poured milk into a cup. 'Daniel not down yet?' She picked up the teapot.

'Gone off to London. Should be back tomorrow night.'

'London?' Katherine spilt tea into the saucer. 'I didn't know he was going away.'

'Nor did I, dear,' Ellen said drily. 'He just appeared with his overnight bag as I was starting breakfast and announced he was off. And, by the look of him, I should say he'd been up most of the night, too.'

Katherine stared down into her cup. There was no earthly reason why Daniel should account for his movements to her. But he could at least have waited to say goodbye, she thought, troubled to realise how much that omission hurt. It had been all too easy to forget over the past few weeks that Daniel had a life about which she knew nothing. Had he gone to see Julia? she wondered drearily.

Mechanically she ate the toast Ellen brought in and then drove Tim to the bus-stop, making a detour on the return journey to check on progress with the house.

'Another couple of weeks and there's no reason why you shouldn't move back in,' the foreman informed her as they stood outside, watching the thatcher up on the roof. 'The decorators can work around you.'

'Another couple of weeks?' Katherine echoed in surprise. 'Is that all?'

'Always supposing the weather doesn't hold things up.' The foreman scanned the grey sky.

Perhaps the heat wave had broken completely and it would rain for days, Katherine mused as she returned to the van and drove back to Norrington Hall. Heavens above, what was wrong with her? She ought to be delighted that the work was progressing so quickly, should be looking forward to returning home and getting her life back on an even keel. But she wasn't, she admitted with a sense of shock. She felt depressed, and empty. And she'd forgotten to check the greenhouse.

She was missing Daniel already, she thought unhappily. Which was absolutely absurd because he'd only been gone a few hours. And even if he'd still been at Norrington Hall, he would have been closeted in his study by now. How could she possibly be missing him when she saw so little of him anyway? It was utterly crazy. The rain began to fall and she switched on the windscreen wipers. She wouldn't be able to work outside in this; she might just as well go into Salisbury and start looking at wallpaper and curtain material. And there was all the new furniture to buy, she reminded herself without much enthusiasm.

The rain stopped mid-morning and the sun made a watery appearance and, returning from her shopping expedition, Katherine resumed her work in the garden.

'Why don't you stay for the evening?' Ellen invited her as she drove the housekeeper home after dinner. 'Won't you be a bit lonely with both the twins out?'

'No. I'll be fine,' Katherine assured her. There was just the chance that Daniel might telephone ... Then she immediately felt guilty, wondering if the housekeeper was lonely herself and would have liked some company.

She was like a child waiting for Father Christmas, Katherine admonished herself the following evening as she tackled the brambles in the shrubbery. She hadn't been able to settle indoors with a book, couldn't see to concentrate her mind on anything but Daniel. She just ached so much to see him, to hear his deep drawl. She found she was beginning to have imaginary conversations with him in her head, discovered she was trying to imitate some of his expressions as if somehow that could make him feel closer. And all the time was the constant nagging knowledge that she was behaving like a fool. A few weeks' time and she would be back in her own home.

Of course, she would inevitably see Daniel from time to time, but that would be the limit of their association.

She put the safety catch on the secateurs and burst into a grin. Who cared about tomorrow or the next day? Daniel was coming home tonight... She began to walk back towards the house. What time would he be back? Would it look too obvious if she waited up? She went in through the back door and started to wash her hands in the kitchen sink, and then stiffened as through the open window she heard the sound of an approaching car. It could be one of the twins being dropped off... Wiping her hands on the back of her jeans, she sped through the hall and threw open the front door, her eyes riveted to the familiar figure emerging from the red saloon.

She didn't even stop to think, but jumped down the steps two at a time. 'Daniel...' Just in time she came to her senses and resisted the overwhelming longing simply to throw her arms around him and hug him.

'Missed me?' Golden eyes scanned her face.

'Maybe,' she grinned. 'Good trip?' He looked pleased to see her, she thought with fluttering happiness. She watched as he moved back towards the car and went numb with shock as for the first time she registered that Daniel hadn't come home alone. Julia Peterson was sitting in the passenger seat.

CHAPTER EIGHT

'KATHERINE. How are you?' the brunette greeted her with a sugary smile. 'I was so sorry to hear about the fire. Daniel told me all about it.' Julia moved towards Daniel and linked her arm through his. 'Darling, I could murder a gin and tonic. The traffic on the way down...' She arched her eyebrows.

'I'll bring our bags in and put the car away,' Daniel smiled down at her. 'Go on in, Ju. You know where everything is. I'll have my usual. Join us for a drink, Katherine?'

'No, thanks.' The stiff little smile was beginning to make her jaw ache. 'I was just about to have a bath.' She spun round and headed straight for the stairs, fighting the urge to break into a run, although she very much doubted that either Julia or Daniel would have noticed if she had. She had no justification for feeling so angry, so hurt. She had no claim on Daniel. He had the perfect right to invite whomsoever he chose into his own home. Opening her bedroom door, she flung herself down on the bed.

Two nights ago Daniel had given her reason to suppose that he wasn't completely averse to her company, that he felt some spark of physical attraction. And on that briefest of foundations she'd built a skyscraper. He hadn't deceived her, given her any false promises... Her hands clenched into fists. Oh, why did he have to bring Julia Peterson back home with him? Couldn't he have simply stayed in London with her? She swung her legs

to the floor and started pacing around the room. She
couldn't spend the night under the same roof as Daniel
and Julia. She pressed a hand to her forehead. So what
exactly did she propose to do? Wait until the twins returned home and then cart them off to a hotel for the
night? Home! Why did she keep calling Norrington Hall
home in her head? It wasn't her home and never would
be. Marching into the bathroom, she slammed the door
resoundingly behind her.

How could she look so disgustingly healthy this morning?
Katherine demanded silently, staring at her reflection in
the dressing-table mirror. She felt pale, washed out, but
her honey-golden skin was exactly the same shade as it
had been yesterday. The faint shadows under the eyes
were the only tell-tale sign of her sleepless night, but
even they were only noticeable under very close
inspection.

Vigorously she began to brush her hair, sweeping the
corn-coloured waves back over her shoulder. She rose
to her feet, removed her robe, and slipped on the green
cotton dress with the flattering scooped neckline over
her head. Picking up her one and only lipstick, she began
to apply it to her lips and then paused. What on earth
was she playing at? Abruptly she pulled out a tissue from
the box and wiped it over her mouth, and then, un-
zipping the dress, tossed it on the bed.

She couldn't compete with Julia Peterson, so why even
bother trying? Besides which, the twins were going to
notice if she turned up for breakfast dressed like a dog's
dinner and were certain to make some tactless comment
on her appearance. She rummaged in her cupboard for
a clean pair of denims and pulled them up over her
slender hips. She was a faded jeans and T-shirt person

and it was no good her trying to be anything else. If Daniel's taste ran to sophisticated brunettes there was nothing she could do about it. Why should she anyway? She was her, Katherine Maitland, and she wasn't going to change just to attract a mere male.

Closing her door behind her, she began to walk determinedly along the landing.

'Morning, Katherine.'

She turned her head sharply, just in time to see Julia emerging from a door to the right. Daniel's door. The pain was so intense that she felt as if she'd been kicked in the stomach. She'd accepted last night that Julia and Daniel were certain to be sleeping together, so why did the confirmation make it any harder to bear?

Returning a muttered answer, Katherine didn't wait for the other girl to catch up with her, but sped on down the stairs. The thought of breakfast made her feel nauseous. She darted into the morning-room on her left, opened the french windows at the far end and emerged into the garden. She walked furiously around the perimeter of the garden and finally found herself by the swimming pool. Kicking off her sandals, she rolled up her jeans and dangled her legs in the water, staring morosely into the blue depths.

'Katherine?'

She nearly fell forwards into the water as she heard the soft voice behind her. Daniel! The very last person in the world she wanted to see right now.

'What?' she muttered, without looking round.

'You haven't had breakfast. Ellen was wondering where you were.'

She shrugged. 'I'm not hungry.' And if you don't go away I'm going to stand up and push you into the pool, she thought silently.

'So what's wrong?'

'Why the hell should there be anything wrong just because I don't feel like breakfast for once?' Abruptly she rose to her feet and slipped on her sandals.

'There's no need to be, you know,' Daniel murmured softly and she stiffened, swinging round to face him.

'Jealous,' he continued in the same quiet, even tone. 'Of Julia.'

'Jealous?' She gave a brittle laugh, which somehow ended as a choke. 'Don't be ridiculous...' She flinched as he put out a hand and touched her cheek.

'Admit it, Kat. You're jealous as hell.'

She felt the hot colour stinging her face and knew that she had completely betrayed herself. 'Please, just go away,' she mumbled. 'Just leave me.' Why was he trying to humiliate her like this?

'Julia is an old friend. Nothing more.' Very gently he pushed her down into one of the wicker chairs and dropped to his haunches beside her, so that their faces were on a level.

'But I saw her... coming out of your room this morning.'

'Mmm. And if you'd waited another couple of minutes you'd have seen her husband coming out behind her. Mike arrived late last night. He and Julia are spending a couple of days here before going on to their cottage in Cornwall.' He shrugged. 'I gave them my room as it's the only one with a double bed.'

Katherine stared at him. 'At James's wedding Julia gave me the impression that you and she were having an affair... and then the day I came over to talk to you about Jessica she arrived and I saw you both together...'

'Put-up job,' he said calmly, picking up her hand and holding it between his two larger ones.

'You mean you deliberately tried to make me jealous?' Katherine gazed at him incredulously.

'Mmm,' he agreed, unabashed. 'Childish, hmm? But effective.' His thumb caressed the back of her hand. 'As well as being a good friend, Julia also happens to be my solicitor and has been handling my divorce.' He quirked a dark eyebrow. 'The decree absolute was granted yesterday.'

'Oh.' She was bewildered, utterly confused by this conversation. 'I'm sorry,' she said after a long pause. 'That your marriage didn't work out.'

'Are you?' he enquired softly.

'No,' she admitted, lowering her eyes. 'I mean, I'm sorry if anyone was hurt, but...' She couldn't honestly say she was sorry that Daniel no longer had a wife. 'Why did it go wrong so quickly? You were married such a short time.'

'Maria and I married for the wrong reasons,' he said quietly. 'I think we both realised more or less straight away...' A shadow passed over his face and then vanished. 'But I shan't make the same mistake next time.'

'So you're not deterred for life?' Katherine said lightly. 'There's going to be a next time?'

Daniel looked at her contemplatively. 'That,' he murmured, rising to his feet and pulling her up with him, 'all depends on you, Miss Maitland.' Dropping a hand to her waist, he drew her against him. 'That is supposed to be a proposal,' he added conversationally.

'What?' Everything was happening too fast. 'You're asking me to marry you?' She felt dizzy as she saw the truth in the golden eyes. 'But why?'

'I need a permanent gardener,' he teased. 'And I also happen to love you very much.' Lowering his head, he kissed her gently and then with an increasing urgency that made the blood rush to her head. 'I've been wanting to do that for weeks,' he said huskily, lifting his head.

'So why didn't you?' Katherine asked shakily. 'The other night...'

He dropped into a wicker chair and pulled her on to his knee, cradling her in his arms. 'You were under my roof, my protection,' he said quietly. 'I was also still technically a married man.' He stroked back a tendril of hair from her face. 'I knew you were attracted to me...'

'You arrogant...' Katherine kissed him soundly on the mouth. Why deny it? He was simply being honest. Of course, he must have realised by her response every time he touched her that she wasn't exactly immune to him. How wonderful just to be able to kiss him, touch him without restraint. He was hers. A wave of delirious happiness engulfed her.

'But I wanted more than that from you,' he continued softly. 'I didn't want just an affair, a meaningless physical relationship.'

'I would never have...' she protested heatedly, and then again admitted he was right. If Daniel had persisted in his attentions she wouldn't have had the strength to resist for long.

'It's not just women who need an emotional commitment,' he murmured. He grinned down at her. 'Do you know, I've done hardly any work at all since you've been living here?'

'But you've been in your study practically the whole time!' she protested.

'And most of the time I've been staring out of the window instead of working on my lecture notes. Just knowing how close you were was enough to distract me completely.'

She looked at him wonderingly, unable to believe that she could have that a disruptive effect on his work. 'And there was me thinking you'd turned into a workaholic,' she chided him with a smile, and then frowned. 'Lecture notes?'

'Mmm.' He sighed. 'I've accepted an invitation to do an extended lecture tour of the States and Canada this autumn. Bad timing, eh?'

'How long for?' She couldn't bear to lose him, not so soon.

'A few months, I'm afraid.' His eyes darkened. 'I can't let everyone down at this late stage. But I'll be home by Christmas.'

She nodded. She didn't want to think about that right now, didn't want anything to spoil these wonderful moments.

'You really love me?' She just wanted to hear him say those magical words again—in fact, over and over again. She would never get tired of hearing them.

'Yes, Kat, I love you. I think I always have. As a child, you were like the kid sister I never had.' He smiled reflectively. 'Following me around on your sturdy little legs.'

'You were always kind. Never told me to get lost,' she remembered.

'And then you grew up,' he said wryly. 'And one day I realised I was looking at a woman, realised that my feelings for you were no longer that of a brother, but those of a man.'

'But why didn't you say anything?'

'You wouldn't let me anywhere near you. Practically used to run a mile if you saw me.'

'I was scared to death of the way I felt,' she said quietly and paused. 'I thought you hated me. Because of your leg.'

His arms tightened round her. 'I never blamed you for that. The tennis was never that important. I doubt I would have made the grade anyway. I was just a big fish in a small pool for a while, that's all.'

'But why would you never talk to me about it?' she demanded, thinking of all the pain and misery that could have been avoided. 'For a while I used to feel as if you couldn't even bear to look at me.'

He nodded. 'I couldn't,' he said frankly. 'Every time I saw you it just reminded me of the accident. Reminded me how nearly you could have been killed.' He smiled. 'Perhaps even then I knew that you were going to be the most important thing in my life.'

Katherine nestled up to him. The most important thing in his life. Her.

'So you will marry me?'

'Mmm. Yes, please.' She raised her lips expectantly, murmuring contentedly as his mouth took possession of hers.

'I think I'll let the house for the time being,' Katherine murmured thoughtfully. 'Maybe sell it later when the twins are older.'

'Sounds sensible,' Daniel agreed.

He was sitting on the sofa, completing the crossword in the newspaper, while she sat on the carpet by his feet, gazing into the flickering flames of the wood fire. The evenings were growing cooler, the distinct scent of autumn beginning to linger in the air.

Katherine wriggled her toes. Being here like this with Daniel was heaven. It didn't seem to matter that they weren't actually touching, weren't even talking much. Just being close to him was enough.

The last two weeks had passed in a blur of undiluted happiness, a happiness that seemed to be shared by all those closest to her. Ellen, the twins, now at college, Daniel's parents—all had been delighted with the news of their engagement. And not, Katherine remembered, particularly surprised.

'About time, too,' the twins had commented when she'd broken the news.

'I always knew you and Daniel would come to your senses one day,' Mrs Sinclair had confessed.

Katherine smiled, studying the diamond ring on her left hand. She still felt a moment of disbelief every time she saw it, still couldn't quite believe that this happiness was here to stay.

'What?'

She looked up at Daniel as she heard him mutter under his breath.

'Pen's run out.' He bent his head and kissed her parted lips. 'Do you love me?'

'Mmm.'

'Enough to go and fetch me another pen?' His mouth curved into a teasing grin; the gold-flecked hazel eyes danced.

Look at me like that and I'd jump into Niagara Falls for you, she thought, loving him so much that it hurt.

'Lazy pig,' she admonished him, rising to her feet and tossing a cushion at his head. 'Is that what you want a little wifey for, to run and carry for you?'

'That, among other things,' he agreed solemnly. 'There should be a stack of pens in the study.'

'I'm to be allowed in the inner sanctum?' Katherine raised her eyebrows and, avoiding his outstretched hand, danced to the door.

She pushed open the study door and flicked on the light. A drawing-board set up near the window dominated the room. A computer stood on a table beside it and at the far end of the room was a large walnut desk strewn with papers. No immediate sign of a pen anywhere. Heavens, how could Daniel work in this chaos?

She pulled open one of the desk drawers, found it contained nothing more than envelopes, tried the next one and stiffened as she saw the bundle of photographs lying face up. Without moving, she stared down at the one uppermost. Daniel, formally attired in a dark suit and buttonhole standing on the steps of an unidentifiable building beside a small fair-haired young woman in a cream suit, clutching a posy of flowers in her gloved hands.

Daniel and Maria on their wedding-day. It had to be. She swallowed hard. Why had Daniel kept the photograph? Nostalgia? Maybe his marriage had been short-lived, but for a while at least this other woman must have been important to him. Odd. Maria looked so completely different from her mental image of her. For a start, she was fair, not a brunette.

Hating herself but not able to fight the temptation to learn more about Daniel's past life, she picked up the photographs. She stared for a long time at Maria. This woman had shared Daniel's life, albeit fleetingly. Slowly she moved on to the next photograph and her breath lodged in her throat. Maria, smiling at the camera, a baby in her arms.

For a second Katherine couldn't move, her brain seemed to stop functioning, and then in a swift, jerky movement she spread the remainder of the photographs across the table. Maria with a small child on her lap; Maria, pushing a toddler on a swing, playing with it in a sand pit. Not an it. A child. A boy. A boy with dark red curls. Weakly she turned over the last photograph: 'Johnny, aged four.'

'Katherine, couldn't you find a pen?'

She jumped as she heard the voice behind her but didn't turn round. 'Why didn't you tell me you had a child?'

'What?' She sensed Daniel coming up beside her, realised he had now seen the photographs strewn over his desk.

'You've been through my desk?'

She swivelled around to face him, saw the anger in his eyes. 'Damn your privacy,' she said thickly. 'Why the hell didn't you tell me about J-Johnny? Is that why you married Maria? Because she was carrying your child? And then what happened? Did you make her feel she'd trapped you, make life so unbearable for her that she left? What do you do, send them both money to ease your guilt in return for a few photographs?' She began to shake uncontrollably.

'Katherine——'

'No!' She shrank from Daniel's hand and, jumping to her feet, pushed past him and ran blindly out into the hall. Hardly registering what she was doing, motivated simply by the driving need to be on her own and as far away from Daniel as possible, she grabbed her van keys from the hall table and charged out of the front door.

She had no idea of where she was going, Katherine realised, had been driving around in aimless circles for what seemed like eternity. Daniel had a son. Why hadn't he told her? That's what really hurt. And she was jealous, she admitted. Jealous that some woman she'd never met would always have part of the man she loved. Because she still loved him. Nothing could change that. If only she could talk to someone... James. She would go and see James. She swung the car around and headed back towards the small town.

She drove slowly down James's road, checking that the downstairs lights were still on before drawing to a halt in front of his cottage. She clambered out, sped up to the front door and rang the bell and instantly regretted it. She shouldn't be bothering James with her problems at this time of night, should have the maturity to work them out for herself, but it was too late to turn away now, as the door was opening.

'James, I'm sorry...' she began, and swallowed hard, fighting back the tears.

'Hey, come on in. Robyn, it's Kat.' Putting an arm across her shoulder, he led Katherine through into the sitting-room.

'I'm sorry,' Katherine began again as she saw Robyn curled up in her dressing-gown on the sofa. 'I didn't realise it was so late,' she mumbled, catching sight of the clock on the mantelpiece.

'Coffee?' Robyn rose to her feet, and Katherine saw the look of complete understanding that passed between husband and wife. They had no secrets from each other, she thought, fighting back the choking tears.

'So what's up?' James said gently. 'Daniel?'

She nodded. She was beginning to feel a complete and utter fool.

'Want to tell me about it?'

Katherine looked into the warm brown eyes. No, she didn't want to talk about it, she realised. It was something she had to sort out with Daniel. She shouldn't have rushed away like that, should have stayed and at least given him a chance to explain.

'Does Daniel know where you are?'

'No.' She grimaced. 'I just stormed out a couple of hours ago.'

'I think I'll give him a ring,' James decided. 'He'll be worried sick by now.'

'Will he?' she said drearily. 'Thanks,' she added as Robyn appeared with a mug of coffee. 'I'm...'

'If you apologise once more I'm going to hit you over the head,' the New Zealand girl said cheerfully. 'Hey, you and I are going to be sisters-in-law soon...'

'Maybe.' She wasn't sure about anything any more.

'James and I were always falling out just before the wedding,' Robyn grinned. 'Par for the course. And fun making up.'

Katherine forced a smile to her lips. How would you react if you suddenly found out that James had a son? she wondered silently. She looked up as James returned to the room. 'Drink your coffee and then I'll drive you home,' he said quietly.

'I can drive myself...' she protested.

He smiled. 'Orders from big brother!'

Daniel must have heard the car because as James drew up outside Norrington Hall the front door opened.

'Thanks,' Katherine mumbled to James and scrambled out of the car, walking slowly towards the figure towering in the doorway. She'd expected Daniel to be angry, but his face was a blank mask, devoid of all expression. Wordlessly she followed him through into the drawing-room and sat down on a chair.

'Drink?'

She shook her head, watching as he poured himself a large whisky and, keeping the bottle with him, sat down opposite her.

'I shouldn't have run off like that.' Someone had to start the conversation.

'Run to James, you mean?' A muscle flickered in the line of his jaw. 'Nothing's changed, has it, Kat?'

She frowned. 'What do you mean?'

'It's always been James. And it always will be. The night your parents were killed...' He threw back the whisky. 'Remember? James and I both came over straight away...but it was James you immediately turned to.' He gave a tight smile. 'Even after James was married, the day of the fire, it was still him you kept asking for... and now tonight...'

'He's my best friend, that's all.'

'Shouldn't the man you're going to marry be your best friend?' he said quietly. 'My God, you didn't even wait to talk to me tonight.' He poured out another shot of whisky.

'I was hurt...' she muttered defensively. 'You should have told me...'

'Johnny's not my son,' he said flatly. Dark eyebrows drew together in a line across his forehead. 'My God, don't you think if I'd had a child I would have mentioned it? Do you think I'd have been content with the occasional photograph if Johnny had been my son?'

She lowered her eyes, flushing with shame.

'Just after your parents were killed I went to Canada. I thought you blamed me for their death... God, I wanted so much to look after you then, to comfort you, but all you wanted was James.' He shrugged resignedly. 'I met Maria a few weeks later. She moved into the apartment next to mine. With Johnny, who was just a few months old. Her nephew.' He paused. 'She was a widow. Her husband, her husband's brother and his wife, who happened to be Maria's sister, were all killed in a car crash in which only Maria and Johnny survived.' He rose to his feet and began pacing up and down the room. 'By sheer fluke, I happened to bear a slight resemblance to Maria's husband.'

'Your hair...' Katherine mumbled, suddenly understanding. Maria's husband and her brother-in-law had possessed the red hair inherited by Johnny. Because of that one common factor with Daniel she'd jumped to the completely wrong conclusion about the boy's paternity.

'Yes,' he said shortly. 'She was alone and desperately unhappy and I happened to be there.' He threw himself back into his chair. 'She needed someone...in her emotional state I think she even confused me with her husband at times in her mind. And I wanted to be needed.' His voice softened. 'She reminded me so much of you. Her circumstances were so similar to the ones in which I'd just left you...but, unlike you, she turned to me for help and comfort.' He raked a hand through his hair. 'It would have been better if she'd simply moved in with me for a while until we both came to our senses. But there was Johnny to consider as well. So we got married.'

Katherine stared down at her hands, thinking of Maria and her appalling loss. How could she bear it if anything ever happened to Daniel?

'We both realised we'd made a mistake. Maria was still in love with her husband. I couldn't fill the void...and I was in love with you. We agreed to go our separate ways before Johnny was old enough to be affected. Maria went home to live with her parents.'

'But you still keep in touch?'

He nodded. 'I shall always care what happens to her.'

'Yes,' Katherine said quietly. She wouldn't want it otherwise, wouldn't want Daniel to be anything less than the compassionate, honourable man he was. How could she even for a moment have thought...? 'Why didn't you tell me all this before?' she asked in subdued voice.

'I would have when the time seemed right,' he said after a long pause. 'It was a chapter in my life of which I'm not particularly proud. And I suppose I didn't want to rake up the past, bring back memories of your parents' death.'

'I'm sorry,' she muttered gruffly. That's all she seemed to be doing this evening, apologising. About everything.

He shrugged, and rose to his feet. 'I'm going up to London tomorrow. I'll stay with Julia and Mike until I fly off to the States.'

'Daniel!' Katherine jumped up and raced out into the hall after him. 'But why? I said I was sorry...'

'And that changes everything?' An expression of utter weariness crossed his face. 'What chance does our marriage have if every time we have a problem you go rushing off to James?'

Katherine's face tightened. She'd apologised, admitted she had been in the wrong—what else did he want? Damn it, she wasn't going to crawl to him. If he didn't love her enough to forgive her then he was right, their marriage didn't stand a snowball's chance in hell. Wrenching the ring off her finger, she thrust it into his hand.

'You don't have to go to London to escape me. The twins and I will move back home tomorrow,' she muttered through stiff, parched lips, and tore up the stairs.

Katherine turned up the collar of her jacket against the biting wind as she walked briskly along the high street. Only the beginning of December, and already the shops were decorated for the festive season. Christmas. She was dreading it. And New Year's Eve was going to be even harder to cope with. She saw the bundled figure coming towards her and smiled in greeting.

'Hello, Ellen.'

'Cold enough for you?' The older woman blew on her mittened hands. 'You left your scarf last Sunday when you came to tea. I've been meaning to drop it in.'

'I'll pop by and pick it up.' She glanced at her watch. 'I've just a few errands to run. How about meeting for a cup of tea in the Copper Kettle in about half an hour, if that suits you, and I'll give you a lift home?'

'That would be nice, dear. See you in a little while.'

Katherine continued along the pavement. She'd grown increasingly fond of Ellen over the last few months. At first she'd been wary of visiting her, dreading that Ellen might mention Daniel and yet at the same time longing to hear news of him. Time hadn't lessened the pain inside her, but it had brought a kind of passive acceptance. Daniel, for all his avowals, quite simply hadn't really loved her, or at least not enough, and there was nothing in the world she could do to change that. There was no point in dwelling on the happiness that she'd had so fleetingly in her grasp. She simply had to get on with her life, put the past and Daniel behind her. Of course, it wasn't easy. There were times she ached so much inside that she could have yelped out loud with the pain. But she was trying, she told herself firmly. And that was the first step in the long road to recovery.

She arrived at the tea-shop first and ordered tea for two and a selection of cakes, and settled down to wait for Ellen, watching the passers-by through the window. She jerked her head forward as a man strode by with long, loping strides. This was always happening. She'd see a head in a crowd, the expression on someone's face...and her heart would stop.

'Have you been waiting long, dear?'

'No.' Katherine looked up with a smile as Ellen joined her. 'I've ordered some cakes.' She grinned. 'Felt like being a real pig.'

'Nothing like a bit of stodge to keep the cold out,' Ellen said comfortably. 'And you could certainly do with a bit more insulation,' she observed. 'You're getting too thin. And you're looking tired,' she added reprovingly.

'Stayed up late last night reading a whodunit.' Katherine shrugged dismissively. OK, she was finding it difficult to sleep at night. But she wasn't lying in bed tossing and turning, thinking about Daniel. She was doing something positive, working her way through the thriller section at the local library. 'I've been meaning to ask you...' she smiled her thanks as the waitress placed a tray on the table '...what you're doing for Christmas. Because if you're not doing anything special, would you like to come to spend the day with me and the twins?'

'I'd love to.'

'Good.' Katherine smiled. Ellen looked quite misty-eyed, seemed really touched by the invitation. She should have extended it sooner. How awful it must be to have no family at all at a time like Christmas, not to be sur-rounded by the people you loved most in the world. Oh,

God, she wished she could just close her eyes and wake up in the first week of January.

She dropped Ellen off at her cottage and drove on home through the growing darkness. Lights twinkled from the windows as she parked the van in the drive. The twins must be back from college. She hadn't realised it was so late. Hopefully Tim had lit the fire in the sitting-room.

She walked around to the side of the house, surprised not to find Tim and Jessica in the kitchen devouring huge chunks of bread and jam, as they usually did when she wasn't there to direct them towards the fruit bowl.

'Hi, I'm home.' She placed two shopping bags on the table and began to store the contents in the cupboard. She heard the kitchen door open but didn't turn round. 'I saw Ellen in town. That's why I'm a bit late. We went for a cup of tea.'

'Hello, Kat.'

She froze. No. It couldn't be. She was imagining it, hearing the deep voice as she so often did in her dreams. Slowly she turned round.

'Daniel.' She couldn't move, couldn't do anything but stare at him.

'I said I'd be back by Christmas.' He took a step towards her, his eyes searching her face. 'God, I've missed you.'

'Have you?' she croaked. Damn it, he had no right just to walk back into her life like this, as if nothing had happened, as if it had been days rather than months since she'd last seen him. Surely he wasn't expecting her to throw herself into his arms with cries of unrestrained joy?

'Oh, Daniel!' She launched herself across the floor towards him.

He crushed her against him so hard that she could hardly breathe, raining kisses on her face.

'I've been such a fool,' he muttered hoarsely. 'Can you ever forgive me? I was so angry. Hurt. I just wanted to block you out of my mind. But I couldn't. I've never been able to do that, although God knows I've tried hard enough over the years.'

'But why didn't you even write?'

'I wrote dozens of letters and tore them up. I began to wonder if I'd taken things too quickly, simply caught you on the rebound from James.'

Katherine's heart twisted as she saw the uncertainty in his eyes. 'I never loved James,' she said softly. 'It's always been you.'

'Do you know what it's like to be jealous of your own brother?' he said simply.

'There was never any need. I love you, Daniel.'

'Do you know, that's the first time you've actually said those words to me?' He bent his head and sought her mouth in a long, lingering kiss.

'Can we come in now before this gets X-rated? We're starving.'

Simultaneously Daniel and Katherine raised their heads and surveyed the twins' grinning faces.

Next Month's Romances

Each month you can choose from a wide variety of romance with Mills & Boon. Below are the new titles to look out for next month, why not ask either Mills & Boon Reader Service or your Newsagent to reserve you a copy of the titles you want to buy — just tick the titles you would like and either post to Reader Service or take it to any Newsagent and ask them to order your books.

Please save me the following titles:	Please tick	√
RIDE THE STORM	Emma Darcy	
A DAUGHTER'S DILEMMA	Miranda Lee	
PRIVATE LIVES	Carole Mortimer	
THE WAYWARD WIFE	Sally Wentworth	
HAUNTING ALLIANCE	Catherine George	
RECKLESS CRUSADE	Patricia Wilson	
CRY WOLF	Amanda Carpenter	
LOVE IN TORMENT	Natalie Fox	
STRANGER PASSING BY	Lilian Peake	
PRINCE OF DARKNESS	Kate Proctor	
A BRIDE FOR THE TAKING	Sandra Marton	
JOY BRINGER	Lee Wilkinson	
A WOMAN'S LOVE	Grace Green	
DANGEROUS DOWRY	Catherine O'Connor	
WEB OF FATE	Helena Dawson	
A FAMILY AFFAIR	Charlotte Lamb	

If you would like to order these books in addition to your regular subscription from Mills & Boon Reader Service please send £1.70 per title to: Mills & Boon Reader Service, P.O. Box 236, Croydon, Surrey, CR9 3RU, quote your Subscriber No:..............................
(If applicable) and complete the name and address details below. Alternatively, these books are available from many local Newsagents including W.H.Smith, J.Menzies, Martins and other paperback stockists from 6th November 1992.

Name:..

Address:..

....Post Code:........................

To Retailer: If you would like to stock M&B books please contact your regular book/magazine wholesaler for details.

You may be mailed with offers from other reputable companies as a result of this application.
If you would rather not take advantage of these opportunities please tick box ☐

WIN A TRIP TO ITALY

Three lucky readers and their partners will spend a romantic weekend in Italy next May. You'll stay in a popular hotel in the centre of Rome, perfectly situated to visit the famous sites by day and enjoy the food and wine of Italy by night. During the weekend we are holding our first International Reader Party, an exciting celebratory event where you can mingle with Mills & Boon fans from all over Europe and meet some of our top authors.

HOW TO ENTER

We'd like to know just how wonderfully romantic your partner is, and how much Mills & Boon means to you.

Firstly, answer the questions below and then fill in our tie-breaker sentence:

1. Which is Rome's famous ancient ruin?

  ❏ The Parthenon   ❏ The Colosseum   ❏ The Sphinx

2. Who is the famous Italian opera singer?

  ❏ Nana Mouskouri   ❏ Julio Iglesias   ❏ Luciano Pavarotti

3. Which wine comes from Italy?

  ❏ Frascati   ❏ Liebfraumilch   ❏ Bordeaux

Tie-Breaker: Well just how romantic is your man? Does he buy you chocolates, send you flowers, take you to romantic candlelit restaurants? Send us a recent snapshot of the two of you (passport size is fine), together with a caption which tells us in no more than 15 words what makes your romantic man so special you'd like to visit Rome with him as the weekend guests of Mills & Boon.

....

....

....

....

Mills & Boon

In order to find out more about how much Mills & Boon means to you, we'd like you to answer the following questions:

1. How long have you been reading Mills & Boon books?

☐ One year or less ☐ 2-5 years ☐ 6-10 years

☐ 10 years or more

2. Which series do you usually read?

☐ Mills & Boon Romances ☐ Medical Romances ☐ Best Seller

☐ Temptation ☐ Duet ☐ Masquerade

3. How often do you read them? ☐ 1 a month or less

☐ 2-4 a month ☐ 5-10 a month ☐ More than 10 a month

Please complete the details below and send your entry to: Mills & Boon Reader Service, FREEPOST, P.O. Box 236, Croydon, Surrey CR9 9EL, England.

Name: ....

Address: ....

.... Post Code: ....

Are you a Reader Service subscriber?

☐ No ☐ Yes my Subscriber No. is: ....

_____ RULES & CONDITIONS OF ENTRY _____

1. Only one entry per household.
2. Applicants must be 18 years old or over.
3. Employees of Mills & Boon Ltd., its retailers, wholesalers, agencies or families thereof are not eligible to enter.
4. The competition prize is as stated. No cash alternative will be given.
5. Proof of posting will not be accepted as proof of receipt.
6. The closing date for entries is 31st December 1992.
7. The three entrants with correct answers who offer tie-breaker sentences considered to be the most appropriate and original will be

judged the winners.
8. Winners will be notified by post by 31st January 1993.
9. The weekend trip to Rome and the Reader Party will take place in May 1993.
10. It is a requirement of the competition that the winners attend the Reader Party and agree to feature in any publicity exercises.
11. If you would like your snapshot returned, please enclose a SAE and we'll return it after the closing date.
12. To obtain a list of the winning entries, send a SAE to the competition address after 28th February, 1993.

You may be mailed with offers from other reputable companies as a result of this application. Please tick the box if you would prefer not to receive such offers. ☐

BARBARY WHARF

WORLDWIDE

BY CHARLOTTE LAMB

BY POPULAR DEMAND
An exciting new saga by one of the world's bestselling writers of romance.

Besieged
CHARLOTTE LAMB
An exciting new saga by one of the world's bestselling writers of romance.
BARBARY WHARF
BOOK ONE

BARBARY WHARF
2
An exciting new saga by one of the world's bestselling writers of romance.
Battle for Possession
Charlotte Lamb

MINI SERIES

BARBARY WHARF is an exciting new six book mini series set in the glamorous and fast-paced world of International Journalism.

There are six books in the series begining with **BESEIGED** and continuing with **BATTLE FOR POSSESSION**. The drama will develop each month, with every novel featuring an INDEPEN-DENT and romantic love story.

DON'T MISS THIS EXCITING SERIES - ORDER YOUR COPIES TODAY! (see over for details).

BARBARY WHARF

W⦿RLDWIDE

BRAND NEW MINI SERIES

As you know there are six books in total. Why not reserve your copies and receive two each month from Mills & Boon Reader Service for only £2.99 each, postage and packing FREE, or enclose a cheque for £17.94 made payable to Mills & Boon to receive all six books at once. Either way you will not miss any of these exciting future titles.

To reserve your **BARBARY WHARF** series, simply complete the coupon below and return it to:-
Mills & Boon Reader Service,
FREEPOST PO Box 236, Croydon, CR9 9EL.

MINI SERIES

- ✂ - -

PLEASE TICK ONE BOX ONLY:

☐ **YES!** Please reserve me a subscription to the **BARBARY WHARF** mini series. I understand that you will send me two books each month and invoice me for £5.98.   **EPBW1**

☐ **YES!** Please send me all six books in the **BARBARY WHARF** mini series. I enclose a cheque for £17.94. Postage and packing free.   **EPBW2**

Ms/Mrs/Miss/Mr _____

Address _____

_____

_____ Postcode _____

Signature _____   Are you a Reader
Service Subscriber   Yes ☐   No ☐

Subscription No. _____

mps MAILING PREFERENCE SERVICE

Offer expires 31st. December 1992. The right is reserved to refuse an application and change the terms of this offer. You may be mailed with offers from other reputable companies as a result of this application. If you would prefer not to share this opportunity please tick the box. ☐